# Essential Maths Skills for
# A-Level Psychology

Love it or loathe it, maths is a big deal in the new Psychology AS and A-Levels — without it, you could lose out on 10% of the overall marks.  Ouch.

Not to worry.  This brilliant CGP book explains all the maths you're likely to meet during the course, with plenty of step-by-step examples to show you how it works.

We've also included practice questions (with answers) to make sure you've got to grips with everything.  Those maths marks are looking a lot more achievable all of a sudden...

A-Level revision?  It has to be CGP!

Published by CGP

Editors:
Katherine Faudemer, Ceara Hayden, Rachael Marshall, Kirstie McHale, Sarah Pattison

ISBN: 978 1 84762 324 9

With thanks to Lauren Burns, Ceara Hayden, Teresa Jamieson and Kirstie McHale for the proofreading.
With thanks to Jan Greenway for the copyright research.

Cover image © Andrey Prokhorov/iStockphoto.com

Critical values table on pages 41 and 42 abridged from FC Powell, Cambridge Mathematical and Statistical Tables, Cambridge University Press (1979).

Critical values table on page 44 abridged from Extended Tables of the Wilcoxon Matched Pair Signed Rank Statistic by Robert L McCornack from the Journal of the American Statistical Association © 1965 Taylor & Francis, reprinted by the publisher Taylor & Francis Ltd, http://www.tandfonline.com

Critical values tables on page 48 abridged from Significance Testing of the Spearman Rank Correlation Coefficient by Jerrold H Zar from the Journal of the American Statistical Association © 1972 Taylor & Francis, reprinted by the publisher Taylor & Francis Ltd, http://www.tandfonline.com

Critical values table on page 50 abridged from FC Powell, Cambridge Mathematical and Statistical Tables, Cambridge University Press (1979).

Critical values tables on pages 59 and 60 abridged from Fundamentals of behavioural statistics (3rd Edn.) by R. Runyon and A. Haber © 1976 McGraw-Hill Education.

McGraw-Hill Education makes no representations or warranties as to the accuracy of any information contained in the McGraw-Hill Education Material, including any warranties of merchantability or fitness for a particular purpose. In no event shall McGraw-Hill Education have any liability to any party for special, incidental, tort, or consequential damages arising out of or in connection with the McGraw-Hill Education Material, even if McGraw-Hill Education has been advised of the possibility of such damages.

Clipart from Corel®
Printed by Elanders Ltd, Newcastle upon Tyne.

Based on the classic CGP style created by Richard Parsons.

# Contents

# Using a Scientific Calculator

*Knowing your way around a calculator will make the mathsy bit of Psychology a lot more straightforward,*
*so grab yourself a scientific calculator and hold on tight...*

## Get Familiar With How Your **Calculator** Works

Depending on the calculator you have, these buttons might
be in **different places**, but they'll work in the **same** way.

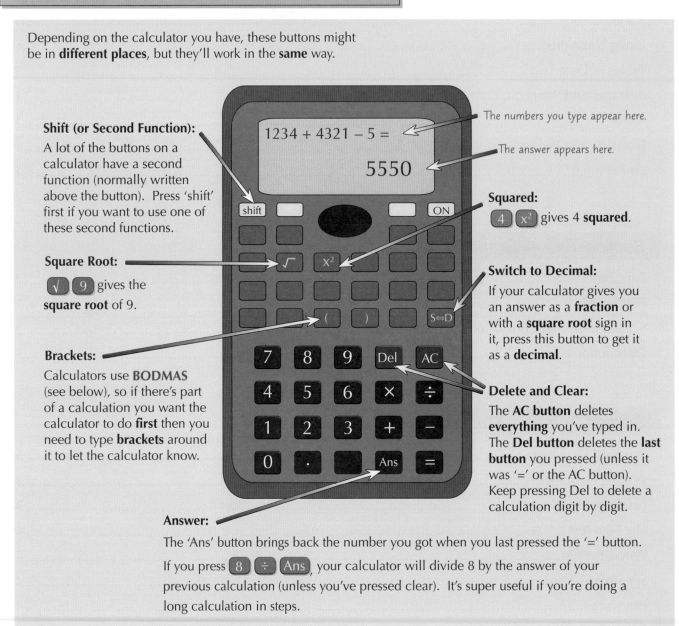

The numbers you type appear here.

The answer appears here.

**Shift (or Second Function):**
A lot of the buttons on a
calculator have a second
function (normally written
above the button). Press 'shift'
first if you want to use one of
these second functions.

**Square Root:**
√ 9 gives the
**square root** of 9.

**Brackets:**
Calculators use **BODMAS**
(see below), so if there's part
of a calculation you want the
calculator to do **first** then you
need to type **brackets** around
it to let the calculator know.

**Squared:**
4 $x^2$ gives 4 **squared**.

**Switch to Decimal:**
If your calculator gives you
an answer as a **fraction** or
with a **square root** sign in
it, press this button to get it
as a **decimal**.

**Delete and Clear:**
The **AC button** deletes
**everything** you've typed in.
The **Del button** deletes the **last
button** you pressed (unless it
was '=' or the AC button).
Keep pressing Del to delete a
calculation digit by digit.

**Answer:**
The 'Ans' button brings back the number you got when you last pressed the '=' button.

If you press 8 ÷ Ans, your calculator will divide 8 by the answer of your
previous calculation (unless you've pressed clear). It's super useful if you're doing a
long calculation in steps.

## Calculators do Things in a **Fixed Order**

You need to be careful entering calculations into a calculator — there's a set order that they always work in.

1) First they'll work out anything in **brackets**.
2) Next they'll work out anything you've **squared** or taken
   a **square root** of (this is called a number's **order**).
3) Then they'll do any **division** or **multiplication**.
4) The last things they'll work out are the **additions** and **subtractions**.

You can remember this order as **BODMAS** — **B**rackets, **O**rder, **D**ivision and **M**ultiplication, **A**ddition and **S**ubtraction.

Be **really careful** about remembering to put brackets in where you need them to make sure you get the right answer.

# Using a Scientific Calculator

## Worked Example

Michael types these three calculations into his calculator:

   a) $2^2 + 16 \div 2 + 3$        b) $(2^2 + 16) \div (2 + 3)$        c) $2^2 + (16 \div 2) + 3$

**What answer does he get for each calculation? Why aren't all of the answers the same?**

**1** *Type each calculation into your calculator and press the 'equals' button to find the answer.*

  a)  $2^2 + 16 \div 2 + 3 = \mathbf{15}$     [2] [x²] [+] [1] [6] [÷] [2] [+] [3] [=]    *This is what you'd type into your calculator.*

  b)  $(2^2 + 16) \div (2 + 3) = \mathbf{4}$     [(] [2] [x²] [+] [1] [6] [)] [÷] [(] [2] [+] [3] [)] [=]

  c)  $2^2 + (16 \div 2) + 3 = \mathbf{15}$     [2] [x²] [+] [(] [1] [6] [÷] [2] [)] [+] [3] [=]

**2** *Use BODMAS to see why the answers aren't always the same.*

Remember, the order for calculations is **B**rackets, **O**rder, **D**ivision, **M**ultiplication, **A**ddition, **S**ubtraction.

  a)  In this calculation there are no brackets, so the first thing the calculator does is find $2^2$.
      The next step is division, so the next thing the calculator does is find $16 \div 2$.
      Finally, the calculator does the additions.

$$2^2 = 4$$
$$16 \div 2 = 8$$
$$4 + 8 + 3 = \mathbf{15}$$

  b)  In calculation b) there are two sets of brackets.
      Inside each set of brackets, the calculator uses the BODMAS order too.
      Then the calculator does the division.

$$(2^2 + 16) \div (2 + 3)$$
$$(4 + 16) \div 5$$
$$20 \div 5 = \mathbf{4}$$

Maria's calculator didn't have as many buttons as her friends', but it did have a lovely varnish.

  c)  In calculation c) the calculator works out the brackets first.
      Then it does the 'order'.
      Lastly, the calculator does the addition.

$$(16 \div 2) = 8$$
$$2^2 = 4$$
$$4 + 8 + 3 = \mathbf{15}$$

In b) and c), adding in brackets changes the order that the calculator solves the problem.
For b) this **changes the answer** from a), but for c) it doesn't.

This is why you need to be **really careful** about where you put the brackets when you're typing a calculation into your calculator — in some places they won't make a difference but in other places they'll have a **big effect** on your answer.

## *My second function is switching off...*

*It's not the most thrilling topic in the world, I'll admit, but it is really important that you can use your calculator properly. Make sure you know where all these buttons are and have a go at using them. If you're feeling really daring, you could even see how adding brackets into some calculations changes the answers you get. You maverick, you.*

# Rounding

*Sometimes a calculation will give you a number with **loads of digits** after the decimal point. Rather than writing them all down, **rounding** can **cut out** a load of those digits while keeping the **value** of the number roughly the **same**. Neat.*

## Rounding Gives *Long Numbers* A *Sensible Length*

The Body Mass Index of a participant is found by the calculation: 63 kg ÷ 3.24 m$^2$

63 kg ÷ 3.24 m$^2$ = $19.4444444444444444444444444...$ kg/m$^2$

As the digits go further to the right, they get smaller in value.

The answer rounded to **ten** digits after the decimal place is: $19.4444444444$ kg/m$^2$

More digits makes the rounded answer more accurate as it is closer to the real value of the answer.

The answer rounded to **five** digits after the decimal place is: $19.44444$ kg/m$^2$

The answer rounded to **two** digits after the decimal place is: $19.44$ kg/m$^2$

Rounding to fewer digits makes the answer less accurate but the number is easier to use.

## You Can Round to a Certain Number of *Decimal Places*...

Say you were rounding 4.26866 to 2 decimal places. Here's what you'd do:

1) Find the position of the **last digit**.

$$\overset{1\ 2\ 3\ 4\ 5}{4.26866}$$

Start counting from the decimal point. You're rounding to **two** decimal places, so the last digit is the **second** one to the right.

2) Look at the next digit to the **right**. $4.26\textbf{8}66$

The next digit is more than 5, so round the last digit up from 6 to 7.

3) If that digit is **less than 5**, the last digit stays the **same**. If the digit is **5 or more**, round **up** the last digit.

$4.26866 \rightarrow 4.27$

Don't give any more digits after the second decimal place.

## ...or to a Certain Number of *Significant Figures*

Rounding to significant figures is the **same** as rounding to decimal places, except for one thing — instead of counting from the decimal point, start counting from the **first digit** that **isn't zero**.

This is the **first** significant figure — start counting from here.

$$\overset{\qquad\qquad 1\ 2\ 3\ 4\ 5}{0.0020546}$$

These zeros aren't significant figures — they just tell you how small the number is.

Any zeros **after** the first significant figure **are included** as significant figures.

So 0.0020546 to 3 significant figures would be 0.00205.

# Rounding

If you're not told how to round your answer, you can **work out** the number of significant figures that you should round to by looking at the measurements you're using in the calculation.

Just **count** the number of significant figures for each measurement and use the **lowest** number of significant figures for your answer.

For example:   $1.2 \div 1.85 = 0.648648648... = 0.65$

2 significant figures

3 significant figures

So the answer should be rounded to 2 significant figures.

Round the last digit up to 5.

You should always use the lowest number of significant figures because the fewer digits a measurement has, the less accurate it is. Your answer can only be as accurate as the least accurate measurement in the calculation.

## Worked Example

The mean score on a personality test is 6.208743. What is the mean score to:

a)   **3 decimal places?**       b)   **3 significant figures?**

**1** **For part a), find the position of the last digit.**

Start counting from the decimal point.
The last digit is in the third decimal place.

The last digit is 8.

$\overset{1\,2\,3}{6.208743}$

It's helpful to let anyone reading your answer know how you've rounded it — d.p. just stands for decimal places.

**2** **Then look at the next digit to the right to round the number to 3 decimal places.**

The next digit is 7.   6.208743

7 is more than 5, so round the last digit up to 9.

6.208743 = **6.209 (3 d.p.)**

**3** **For part b), find the position of the last digit.**

Start counting from the first digit that isn't a zero.
The third digit along is the third significant figure.

There are no zeros at the start, so the first digit is the first significant figure.

$\overset{1\,\,2\,3}{6.208743}$

The last digit is 0.

s.f. is a short way of saying 'significant figures'. You might also see it written as 'sig. fig.'

**4** **Then look at the next digit to the right to round the number to 3 significant figures.**

The next digit is 8.   6.208743

8 is more than 5, so round the last digit up to 1.

6.208743 = **6.21 (3 s.f.)**

## Practice Questions

Q1 Write down the following amounts:

a)   0.0425 g/cm³ to 2 decimal places       b)   5.1092 cm to 3 significant figures

Q2 George is calculating his BMI by dividing his weight in kilograms by his height in metres squared. His weight is 95.03 kg and his height is 1.80 m.

What is his BMI?   Give your answer to an appropriate number of significant figures.

## My sheepdog's no good at maths — he can only round up...

*Rounding isn't glamorous, I admit, but it comes in really useful when you end up with an answer that's as long as your arm. Don't round any numbers until right at the end of a calculation though, or you'll lose the accuracy of the measurements.*

# Standard Form

*Standard form is useful for writing **very big** or **very small** numbers in a **simpler** way.*

## Standard Form Gets **Rid** of Some **0s**

**Very big** or **very small** numbers can have **loads of zeros** (e.g. 640 000 000 or 0.000000015), but writing them in standard form can be more convenient. It converts the number into one **between 1 and 10**.

The decimal point **moves**, and the zeros are represented by a **power of 10**. For example...

The number of participants in a cross-cultural study is estimated to be 2 400 000.

2 400 000 can be written in standard form like this:

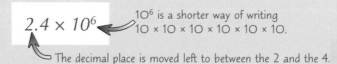

$2.4 \times 10^6$    $10^6$ is a shorter way of writing $10 \times 10 \times 10 \times 10 \times 10 \times 10$.

The decimal place is moved left to between the 2 and the 4.

A psychologist is using a significance level of 0.005 for an inferential test.

0.005 can be written in standard form like this:

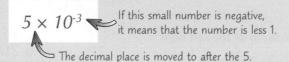

$5 \times 10^{-3}$    If this small number is negative, it means that the number is less 1.

The decimal place is moved to after the 5.

## Numbers in Standard Form Need to be Written in an **Exact Form**

Numbers in standard form will always look like this:

This number is always between **1** and **10**.    $\boxed{A \times 10^n}$    This is the **number of places** the **decimal point** moves. *n* is positive for big numbers, and negative for numbers smaller than 1.

To write a number in standard form, you just have to **count** how many places the decimal point has moved. You also need to know which **direction** it has moved in.

1) If the decimal point has been moved to the **left**, *n* should be **positive**. For example:

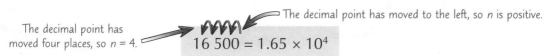

The decimal point has moved four places, so *n* = 4.

The decimal point has moved to the left, so *n* is positive.

$16\ 500 = 1.65 \times 10^4$

2) If the decimal point has been moved to the **right**, *n* should be **negative**. For example:

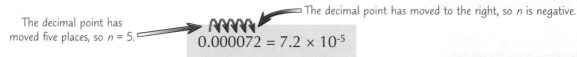

The decimal point has moved five places, so *n* = 5.

The decimal point has moved to the right, so *n* is negative.

$0.000072 = 7.2 \times 10^{-5}$

Your calculator might display a number in standard form like this:

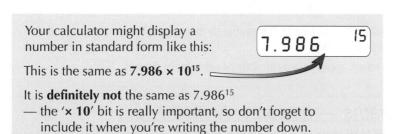

$\boxed{7.986 \quad {}^{15}}$

This is the same as **7.986 × 10¹⁵**.

It is **definitely not** the same as 7.986¹⁵
— the '**× 10**' bit is really important, so don't forget to include it when you're writing the number down.

Gary didn't pay much attention in class, but he was pretty sure his calculation shouldn't include a standing fawn.

# Standard Form

## Worked Example

A patient has been prescribed a drug. The patient's daily dose contains 0.0004 grams of the active ingredient.

a) **Write this amount in standard form.**

b) **The tablets that the hospital stocks each contain $8 \times 10^{-5}$ grams of the active ingredient. How many tablets should the patient be given each day?**

**1** *For part a), count the number of places that the decimal point has to move.*

You want to write 0.0004 in the form $A \times 10^n$.

To make 'A' a number between 1 and 10, you need to place the decimal point **after** the first digit that **isn't a 0**.

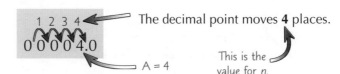

The decimal point moves **4** places.

This is the value for *n*.

**2** *Work out whether n should be positive or negative.*

It's a number smaller than 1, and the decimal point has moved to the **right**, so *n* should be **negative**.

$$0.0004 = 4 \times 10^{-4}$$

**3** *For part b), first write $8 \times 10^{-5}$ as an ordinary number.*

$n = -5$, so the decimal point has been moved **5 places** to the **right**.

To get the normal number, you need to move the decimal point **back 5 places** to the **left**.

$$8 \times 10^{-5} = 0.00008$$

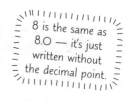

8 is the same as 8.0 — it's just written without the decimal point.

**4** *Divide the number of grams in the dose by the number of grams in each tablet to get the answer.*

The patient has been prescribed **0.0004 grams** of the drug.

You've worked out that there are **0.00008 grams** of drug in each tablet.

$$0.0004 \div 0.00008 = 5 \text{ tablets}$$

## Practice Questions

Q1 Copy and complete the table on the right.

| Ordinary Number | 6120 | | | 0.00000461 |
|---|---|---|---|---|
| Standard Form | | $3.57 \times 10^{-3}$ | $4.782 \times 10^6$ | |

Q2 During a stress experiment the cortisol level in a participant's bloodstream was measured as $1.83 \times 10^{-6}$ g/ml.

a) Write this amount as an ordinary number.

b) The participant's blood cortisol level before the start of the experiment was measured as $6.5 \times 10^{-7}$ g/ml. By how many g/ml did the participant's blood cortisol level increase between the two measurements? Give your answer in standard form.

## I thought a standard form asks for your name and date of birth...

*Don't let standard form bother you — it's really just there to save you writing down a bunch of zeros. If you're doing a calculation with numbers in standard form, just write out the numbers in their ordinary form and work with them. Easy.*

# Using Equations

*In an **equation**, letters take the place of some of the numbers. You're likely to come across equations in Psychology, so it's worth getting familiar with them...*

## An **Equation** Uses **Letters** to Show a **General Rule**

For example, an end of year Psychology mark might be worked out by **adding up** students' scores in two tests. This could be written as an equation like this:

$$M = a + b$$

Where: $M$ is the student's end of year mark,
$a$ is their score in the first test, and
$b$ is their score in the second test.

You could also have something like this:

$$M = 2a + b$$

Or this:

$$M = \frac{\sqrt{a} + b}{2}$$

You can find square roots with your calculator.

$2a$ just means $2 \times a$. You don't need to include the multiply sign when you're multiplying by a letter. So here, you find $M$ by **doubling** $a$ then **adding** $b$.

The line just means **divide** whatever's on top by whatever is underneath. Here, you find $M$ by adding the square root of $a$ to $b$, then dividing the total by 2.

## **Fill In the Values You Know** to Answer Questions Using Equations

Here's how to use an equation:

1) Make sure you know what **each letter** means before you start.
2) **Write down** what number each letter stands for.
3) Write out the equation with **your numbers** in the right place.
4) You'll often be left with just one letter that needs to be replaced with a number. When this happens, you can do the calculation to find the answer.

### Worked Example 1

A psychologist combines participants' scores in two tests using the formula $S = 2a + 3b$, where $S$ is their final score, $a$ is their score in the first test and $b$ is their score in the second test.

**What is the final score of a participant who scored 15 in the first test and 23 in the second test?**

Writing her equations in alphabet spaghetti had seemed like a good idea when she started, but two hours later Alexandra was still hunting for the elusive 'divided by' sign.

**1** ***Write down which numbers match which letters in the equation.***

$a = 15$ and $b = 23$

Matching the right number to the right letter is vital — you'll get a completely different answer otherwise.

**2** ***Write out the equation with your numbers in the place of the letters.***

The equation is: $2a + 3b$    So putting in $a = 15$ and $b = 23$ gives:    $(2 \times 15) + (3 \times 23)$

**3** ***Type the calculation into your calculator to find the answer.***

$2 \times 15 + 3 \times 23 = \mathbf{99}$

Your calculator will do this in the right order because of BODMAS (see page 2).

# Using Equations

## Worked Example 2

A researcher investigated how a person's attitudes towards food related to whether they were obese.
She asked 30 people to fill in a questionnaire, and measured their height and weight.
She then calculated their Body Mass Index (BMI) using the equation:

$$BMI = \frac{w}{h^2}$$

Where:  $w$ = weight in kilograms and
$h$ = height in metres.

A BMI of 30 or higher means a person is clinically obese.
**One of the participants was 180 cm tall, and weighed 90.72 kg.**
**What was their BMI?  Were they clinically obese?**

**1** *Make sure you know what each letter stands for before you start.*

$$BMI = \frac{w}{h^2}$$

$w$ = weight in kilograms
$h$ = height in metres

**2** *Write down which of the numbers in the question matches each letter.*

$w = 90.72$ and $h = 1.8$

If an equation says what units you should be using (like this one says kg and m) make sure your numbers are in these units before you start.  To convert centimetres into metres, divide by 100.  So 180 cm ÷ 100 = 1.8 m

**3** *Write out the equation with the numbers instead of the letters.*

$$BMI = \frac{90.72}{1.8^2}$$

**4** *Type the calculation into your calculator.*

$BMI = 90.72 \div 1.8^2 = \textbf{28}$
28 is less than 30, so this participant was **not clinically obese**.

## Practice Questions

Q1 A personality assessment is made up of three tests scores.
The scores are combined using the equation: $P = 3r \times (s - t)$.
$P$ is the combined score, $r$ is the mark on the first test, $s$ is the mark on the second test and $t$ is the mark on the third test.  A participant scores 2 on the first test, 8 on the second test and 3 on the third test.
Find their combined score.

Q2 A psychologist is developing a new system for measuring IQ.
The system combines the scores from three tests with a person's age, using the equation:

$$I = \frac{6\,(t_1 + t_2 + t_3)}{a}$$

Where:  $t_1$ = their score on test 1,  $I$ = their IQ, and
$t_2$ = their score on test 2,  $a$ = their age in years
$t_3$ = their score on test 3

A participant scores 98 in test 1, 89 in test 2 and 92 in test 3.  He is 18 years old.
According to this equation, what is his IQ?

## I thought the bits with letters were the words, not the sums...

*Equations aren't as bad as they look — you just need to make sure you swap in the right number for each letter.*
*Also, if you're using an equation that has units, make sure your numbers are in the right ones before you use them.*

# Tables of Data

*Tables* are all over the place in Psychology.  Make sure you know how to use them...

## Tables Show Data in Rows and Columns

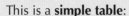

This is a **simple table**:

The **top row** has headings showing what's recorded in each column.

In this table, each row tells you about a **different person**.

This row is for a 22 year old with an aggression score of 2.

| Age (years) | Aggression (measured on a scale of 1-9) |
|---|---|
| 23 | 5 |
| 19 | 3 |
| 22 | 2 |
| 20 | 3 |

Rows go from side to side.

Columns go up and down.

This is a **two-way table**:

Two-way tables have labels **down the side** as well as along the **top**. They are useful when there are two things that you are interested in.

Two-way tables normally show **frequencies** (which just means the number of times something occurs). This table shows the number of people of each gender with low, medium and high aggression scores.

| | Aggression (measured on a scale of 1-9) | | | |
|---|---|---|---|---|
| Gender | 1-3 (low) | 4-6 (medium) | 7-9 (high) | Total |
| Male | 4 | 9 | 2 | 15 |
| Female | 10 | 4 | 1 | 15 |
| Total | 14 | 13 | 3 | 30 |

Two-way tables often have a **total** row and/or column. Lots of statistical calculations need you to use the total, so including these can be really useful.

Look at both sets of labels to see what a number means. This is the number of females with an aggression score of 1-3 (low).

Raw data (the set of individual bits of information collected from each participant) is really difficult to work with — tables are a great way of summarising it.

## Be Careful with the Units

If you're reading from a table...

1) Make sure you **read all the labels** on a table carefully before you start using it.  It saves a lot of trouble later on.

2) Read **down** or **across** from the relevant heading to find the entry you're looking for, paying attention to the **units**.

If you're drawing a table...

Adrian tried to explain to Michelle that this was the wrong sort of table, but she was having none of it.

| Amount of maths in Psychology lesson (%) | Length of fingernails chewed off (mm) |
|---|---|
| 20 | 2 |
| 40 | 3 |
| 95 | 6 |

1) Remember to include a clear heading for each row and/or column.

2) Include the units in the headings for any data that needs them, rather than writing them over and over in the table.  Make sure all the information in a row/column is in the same units.

# Tables of Data

**Worked Example**

A psychologist studying gender differences in exam results recorded the data in the table on the right.

**a) How many males got an A grade?**

**b) How many females did the psychologist study altogether?**

|  | Grade | | | | |
|---|---|---|---|---|---|
| Gender | D | C | B | A | A* |
| Female | 0 | 1 | 3 | 4 | 1 |
| Male | 1 | 1 | 3 | 2 | 2 |

**1** *Find the row showing the grades of the males.*

|  | Grade | | | | |
|---|---|---|---|---|---|
| Gender | D | C | B | A | A* |
| Female | 0 | 1 | 3 | 4 | 1 |
| Male | 1 | 1 | 3 | 2 | 2 |

This row shows the number of males with each grade.

**2** *Read across the row until you reach the column showing the number of A grades.*

|  | Grade | | | | |
|---|---|---|---|---|---|
| Gender | D | C | B | A | A* |
| Female | 0 | 1 | 3 | 4 | 1 |
| Male | 1 | 1 | 3 | 2 | 2 |

This column shows the number of students who got an A grade.

The number of males who got an A grade is the number where the row and the column meet.

**2 males** got an A grade.

**3** *Add up the number of females who got each grade to get the total number that the psychologist studied.*

|  | Grade | | | | |
|---|---|---|---|---|---|
| Gender | D | C | B | A | A* |
| Female | 0 | 1 | 3 | 4 | 1 |
| Male | 1 | 1 | 3 | 2 | 2 |

0 + 1 + 3 + 4 + 1 = 9

**9 females** were studied.

## Practice Questions

Q1 A researcher used a questionnaire to investigate whether video games affect quality of sleep. Some of her results are shown in the table on the right.

a) 12 participants never played video games. Of these, 8 reported having either 1, 2 or 3 nights of disturbed sleep in the last month, 1 reported 4 nights of disturbed sleep and 1 reported 7 nights of disturbed sleep. The rest had no nights of disturbed sleep. Copy the table and add in this missing data.

b) How many participants who played computer games less than once a week (but more often than never) had at least one night of disturbed sleep?

c) How many participants filled in the questionnaire?

d) Do these results suggest that there is a relationship between playing video games and how well you sleep? Explain your answer.

| Frequency of playing video games | Number of nights of disturbed sleep in the last month | | |
|---|---|---|---|
|  | None | 1-3 | More than 3 |
| Once a week or more | 3 | 7 | 2 |
| Less than once a week | 1 | 6 | 1 |
| Never |  |  |  |

## *I can't keep up with your two-way tables...*

*Tables crop up a lot as they're a nice, simple way of showing data, so make sure you know your stuff. If you need to draw one, label it up clearly. And whether you're reading from a table or drawing one, be careful of the units.*

# Averages and Range

*There are three different kinds of average you need to know about — the **mode**, the **median** and the **mean**. Then there's the **range**, too. Best get cracking I think...*

## The **Mode**, **Median** and **Mean** are Different **Averages**

A psychologist investigating the relationship between **foot length** and **vocabulary** in children is analysing his results:

This is the most common foot length.
This is called the **mode**.

Find the **mean** foot length by adding all the children's measurements together and dividing by the number of measurements.

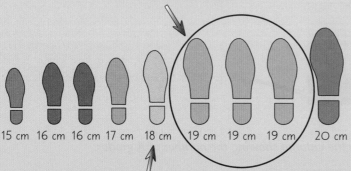

You might have to round your answer — this one actually comes out as 17.666666...

15 cm   16 cm   16 cm   17 cm   18 cm   19 cm   19 cm   19 cm   20 cm

18 cm

This is the middle foot length. If the sizes are arranged in order, like this, it is in the middle of the data set. We call this the **median**.

The **range** is a measure of spread. It is the **difference** between the largest and the smallest number. Here, the range of the lengths is 20 – 15 = **5 cm**.

Averages and the range are a great way of **summarising** a set of data.

## Make Sure You Know How to Find the **Mode**, **Median**, **Mean** and **Range**

1) The **mode** is the **most common value**.

- Count **how many times** each value comes up.
  The number that comes up the **most** times is the mode (or modal value).
- A set of data can have **more than one** mode, e.g. if two values come up the same number of times.
- If all the values in a data set are **different**, there **won't be a mode** at all.

2) The **median** is the **middle value** when the data is arranged in order of size.

- Write out the values in **size order**.
- The median is the **middle value** in this list.
- If you have an **even number** of values, the median is **halfway** between the middle two values.

3) The **mean** is what people normally mean when they say "average".

- Find it using this **equation**: $\text{mean} = \dfrac{\text{total of all the values in your data}}{\text{the number of values in your data}}$

4) The **range** is a measure of how **spread out** your data is.

- Find the range by subtracting the smallest value from the largest.
- The **bigger** the range, the **more spread out** your data is.

*The range is one way of measuring how spread out data is. Another is the standard deviation (see p.34).*

# Averages and Range

## Worked Example

Ten people took a memory test. Their scores were 6, 4, 7, 6, 5, 8, 7, 5, 7 and 9.
**Find the mode, median, mean and range of their scores.**

**1** *Count how many people got each score to find the mode.*

| | |
|---|---|
| 4 — 1 person | 7 — 3 people |
| 5 — 2 people | 8 — 1 person |
| 6 — 2 people | 9 — 1 person |

More people scored 7 than any other number.
**The modal score is 7.**

**2** *Put the numbers in size order to find the median.*

4   5   5   6   (6   7)   7   7   8   9

The middle value is halfway between 6 and 7.
Add 6 and 7 together then divide by two to find it.

$(6 + 7) \div 2 = 6.5$
**The median score is 6.5.**

Nadia was confident her outfit was anything but average.

**3** *Use a calculator to find the mean.*

Add all of the scores together and divide the total by the number of scores (ten).

$(6 + 4 + 7 + 6 + 5 + 8 + 7 + 5 + 7 + 9) \div 10$
$= 64 \div 10 = 6.4$
**The mean score is 6.4.**

**4** *Subtract the smallest score from the largest to find the range.*

The smallest score is 4 and the largest score is 9.

$9 - 4 = 5$
**The range of the scores is 5.**

## Practice Questions

Q1 16 people's scores in an anxiety test are shown on the right.
   a) What is the range of the scores?
   b) What is the mode?
   c) Find the median score.

   15,  7,  2,  5,  9,  3,  5,  6,  5,  4,  6,  2,  8,  12,  3,  8

Q2 A researcher interviewed seven smokers about their smoking habits.
   Each smoker was asked how many cigarettes they had smoked the
   day before the interview. The results are shown on the right.

   20,  16,  8,  14,  17,  12,  9

   a) What is the range of the number of cigarettes the participants had smoked the day before the interview?
   b) What was the mean number of cigarettes the participants smoked? Give your answer to 1 decimal place.

Q3 Thirteen people take part in a memory test. Four people score 14, three people score 16, two people score 13,
   and the other four people score 12, 10, 18 and 15 respectively.
   a) What is the modal score?
   b) What is the median score?
   c) Calculate the mean score. Give your answer to 2 decimal places.

## Working out averages should easily be within your range...

*Mode, median, mean and range. There's a bit to remember here but none of it is that tricky. Just make sure you know which is which, then learn how to work them all out, then hopefully you'll be able to bag yourself a few extra marks in the exams.*

# Ratios

*Ratios help you to compare numbers in different groups...*

## Ratios are a Way of Comparing Quantities

To write a ratio, you just need to write the number of one thing compared to the number of another thing, separated by a **colon**.

Here, for every **two squares** there are **seven circles**. So, the ratio of squares to circles is **2 : 7**.

Now, for every **two squares** there are **eight circles**. So, the ratio of squares to circles is **2 : 8**. However, ratios should be written in their **simplest form**, so this would be written as **1 : 4**.

Ratios don't just have to contain two numbers — they can contain as many numbers as there are categories. The ratio of the shapes below would be written as **1 : 5 : 7**.

In psychology, ratios often come up when comparing **numbers of people in different groups**.

For example, you might compare the number of male respondents to a questionnaire to the number of female respondents. A ratio of 2 : 1 would mean twice as many males had responded as females.

## Write Ratios in Their Simplest Form

Ratios are always written:

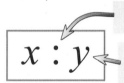

A colon separates one quantity from the other.

*x* and *y* stand for the quantities of each thing, for example, the number of males related to the number of females.

They are more helpful when written in their **simplest form**.
There are two ways to simplify ratios. These are shown in the examples below.

*Even more than her comfortable couch, Jennifer attributed her good relationships with her patients to her firm grasp of ratios.*

### Worked Example 1

As part of a survey, 100 men and 100 women were asked whether they regularly read celebrity magazines. 4 of the men responded 'yes', compared to 36 of the women.
**What is the ratio (written in its simplest form) of men to women who said they regularly read celebrity magazines?**

Be careful when you use ratios to compare numbers like this. If the survey had asked different numbers of men and women, it would be misleading to use a ratio of the number of men who responded 'yes' to the number of women. You need to turn the numbers into percentages first (see page 16) if you are comparing results from groups that aren't the same size.

**1** **Put the numbers into a ratio.**
4 men said they read celebrity magazines regularly, compared to 36 women.
So the ratio is **4 : 36**.
Make sure you get the numbers the right way around — you're asked for the ratio of men to women here.

**2** **Simplify the ratio.**
To get the ratio in its simplest form, divide each side by the same number until you reach the smallest whole number possible on one side.

÷ 4  4 : 36 / 1 : 9  ÷ 4
So the ratio of men to women is **1 : 9**.

# Ratios

**Worked Example 2**

The table on the right shows the number of adults and the number of children in a sample who sleepwalk.
**Calculate the ratio of adult to child sleepwalkers.**
**Give your answer in the form 1 : *n*.**

| | Number that sleepwalk | Number that don't sleepwalk | Total |
|---|---|---|---|
| Adults | 4 | 96 | 100 |
| Children | 17 | 83 | 100 |

**①** *Find the numbers that you need for the ratio.*

First, find the right information in the table.
You want the number of adults that sleepwalk and the number of children that sleepwalk.

Use these numbers to make your ratio. Make sure you get the ratio the right way round — the question asks for the ratio of adults to children.
So, the ratio of adult sleepwalkers to child sleepwalkers is **4 : 17**.

| | Number that sleepwalk | Number that don't sleepwalk | Total |
|---|---|---|---|
| Adults | 4 | 96 | 100 |
| Children | 17 | 83 | 100 |

**②** *Simplify the ratio.*

You might have noticed that this ratio doesn't simplify easily
— you can't divide each side by the same number to get a whole number.
Instead the question asks you to simplify the first number to 1. This means that the second number will become a decimal.

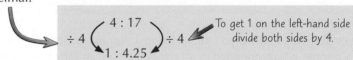

$$\div 4 \begin{array}{c} 4 : 17 \\ 1 : 4.25 \end{array} \div 4$$

To get 1 on the left-hand side divide both sides by 4.

So the ratio of adult to child sleepwalkers is **1 : 4.25**.

## Practice Questions

Q1 The table below shows the number of men and women showing symptoms of obsessive compulsive disorder (OCD) in a sample of 300 people.

a) What is the ratio of people showing symptoms of OCD to those not showing symptoms in this sample?

b) What is the ratio of men showing symptoms to women showing symptoms?

| Gender | Shows symptoms of OCD | Does not show symptoms of OCD | Total |
|---|---|---|---|
| Male | 3 | 147 | 150 |
| Female | 3 | 147 | 150 |
| Total | 6 | 294 | 300 |

Q2 In a memory test, a participant was tested on their memory for words from two lists, each containing 60 words.
He remembered 40 words from the first list and 47 words from the second list.
What is the ratio of words remembered from the first list to words remembered from the second list?
Give your answer in the form 1 : *n*.

Q3 The ratio of male to female participants in a study was 2 : 3.

a) Write this ratio in the form 1 : *n*.

b) If the number of male participants was 30, how many female participants were there?

---

## *The ratio of maths questions I like to those I don't is 1 : 1000...*

*Ratios are just another way of comparing numbers, so don't let the colon throw you off. This stuff could pick you up a few extra marks, so make sure you understand what's going on. Practise simplifying ratios both ways, just in case.*

# Fractions and Percentages

*Fractions* and *percentages* are both ways of showing numbers as a *proportion*.
They come up all the time in Psychology, so it's worth making sure you understand what they are.

## Fractions *and* Percentages *Help You* Compare *Samples of* Different Sizes

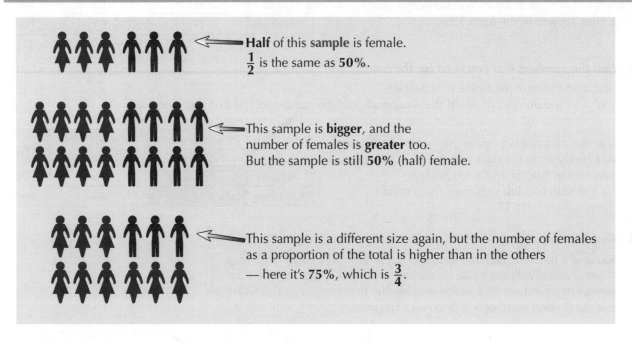

**Half** of this **sample** is female.
$\frac{1}{2}$ is the same as **50%**.

This sample is **bigger**, and the
number of females is **greater** too.
But the sample is still **50%** (half) female.

This sample is a different size again, but the number of females
as a proportion of the total is higher than in the others
— here it's **75%**, which is $\frac{3}{4}$.

Psychologists usually aren't interested in a number by itself — for example, the number of people
in a sample who responded in a certain way. What they really want to know is, for example,
how many people responded in a certain way **compared to the total number of people asked**.
This is why fractions and percentages can be really useful.

## Percent Means 'Out of 100'

Whenever you're doing anything with percentages, you'll have to multiply or divide by one hundred at some point.
Just don't get mixed up:

1)  To show one number as a percentage of another:

    * **Divide** the first number by the second...
    * ...then **multiply** the answer by **100**.

    > 6 out of 10 as a percentage is:
    > $6 \div 10 = 0.6$
    > $0.6 \times 100 = \textbf{60\%}$

2)  To find a percentage of a number:

    * **Divide** the percentage by **100** to get a decimal...
    * ...then **multiply** the number by this decimal.

    > 60% of 10 is:
    > $60 \div 100 = 0.6$
    > $0.6 \times 10 = \textbf{6}$

3)  To find percentage change, there's a handy formula:

    $$\text{percentage change} = \frac{\text{change}}{\text{original}} \times 100$$

    > The percentage decrease
    > from 16 to 10 is:
    > $(16 - 10) \div 16 = 0.375$
    > $0.375 \times 100 = \textbf{37.5\%}$

# Fractions and Percentages

## Worked Example 1

The table on the right shows how participants scored on a memory test.
Scores were given out of 20.
**Complete the table to show each participant's score as a percentage.**

| Participant | Score | Percentage |
|---|---|---|
| 1 | 18 | |
| 2 | 17 | |
| 3 | 13 | |
| 4 | 12 | |
| 5 | 20 | |

*For each entry...*

**1** **Divide the participant's score by the total possible score (20).**

$18 \div 20 = 0.9$

Make sure you do this the right way round — you want to find the participant's score as a percentage of the total possible score.

**2** **Multiply this result by 100.**

$0.9 \times 100 = \textbf{90\%}$

Put the percentages in the table.

| Participant | Score | Percentage |
|---|---|---|
| 1 | 18 | **90%** |
| 2 | 17 | **85%** |
| 3 | 13 | **65%** |
| 4 | 12 | **60%** |
| 5 | 20 | **100%** |

You need to find each of these numbers as a percentage of 20.

## Worked Example 2

85% of the people who filled in a survey were 25 or younger.
In total, 60 people filled out the survey.
**How many people who filled in the survey were 25 or younger?**

**1** **Divide the percentage by 100 to get a decimal.**

$85 \div 100 = 0.85$

**2** **Multiply the total number of people who took part in the survey by this decimal.**

$0.85 \times 60 = \textbf{51 people}$

June suspected Alfred was exaggerating when he told her he was giving his water-skiing lessons 110%.

## Worked Example 3

Emily scored 16 out of 20 in a memory test taken the morning after a good night's sleep.
She retook the test the morning after a night where she hadn't been able to sleep and scored 8 out of 20.
**What was the percentage decrease in her score?**

**1** **Work out how much her score changed by.**

Her score decreased from 16 to 8.     $16 - 8 = 8$

**2** **Plug the numbers into the formula.**

$$\text{percentage change} = \frac{\text{change}}{\text{original}} \times 100$$

$$= \frac{8}{16} \times 100$$

The original value is the score that Emily got the first time around.

**3** **Divide by the bottom number.**   $100 \div 16 = 6.25$

**4** **Multiply by the top number.**

$6.25 \times 8 = 50\%$
Her score decreased by **50%**.

# Fractions and Percentages

## Fractions show a **Part** over the **Total**

- To write one number as a **fraction** of another, stick one on **top** of the fraction and the other on the **bottom**.
- To **cancel down** a fraction, **divide** the top and bottom numbers by the **same thing**.
- To find a fraction of an amount, **multiply** the amount by the fraction's **top** number, and **divide** by the **bottom** number.

### Worked Example 1

Researchers looking into the relationship between stress and major life events recorded whether in the last year workers had taken sick leave, and whether they had moved house. The table on the right shows their results.
**What fraction of the workers in the house-move group took sick leave?**

|  | Sick Leave | | |
| --- | --- | --- | --- |
|  | Yes | No | Total |
| Moved House | 12 | 30 | 42 |
| Control Group | 32 | 102 | 136 |

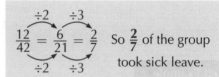

**1** *The number of people in the house-move group who took sick leave goes on top of the fraction. The total number in the house-move group goes on the bottom.*

**2** *Cancel down — divide the top and bottom by the same thing. Keep going until they won't divide any more.*

$$\frac{12}{42} = \frac{6}{21} = \frac{2}{7} \quad \text{So } \frac{2}{7} \text{ of the group took sick leave.}$$

### Worked Example 2

In a sample of 92 people, $\frac{3}{4}$ reported watching television for more than an hour per day.
**How many people in the sample reported watching television for more than an hour per day?**

**1** *Divide the total number of people by the number on the bottom of the fraction.* $\quad 92 \div 4 = 23$

**2** *Then multiply by the number on the top of the fraction.* $\quad 23 \times 3 = \textbf{69}$ people

You need to multiply by the top number and divide by the bottom number, but it doesn't matter which one you do first. Just do it in whichever order is easier.

## Practice Questions

Q1 The table on the right shows the number of people of different ages and genders who completed a questionnaire for a psychological study.

a) What percentage of the people who responded to the survey were in the 21-25 age range?

b) What fraction of the women who responded to the survey were aged between 26 and 35?

|  | Age (years) | | | | |
| --- | --- | --- | --- | --- | --- |
| Gender | 21-25 | 26-30 | 31-35 | 36-40 | Total |
| Male | 20 | 12 | 17 | 14 | 63 |
| Female | 15 | 16 | 15 | 16 | 62 |
| Total | 35 | 28 | 32 | 30 | 125 |

Q2 a) It is estimated that, in the UK, about $\frac{1}{250}$ of females between the ages of 15 and 30 suffer from anorexia nervosa. In a sample of 1000 females aged 15 to 30, how many would you expect to suffer from anorexia nervosa?

b) For males in the same age range, the estimated frequency of anorexia nervosa is 0.05%. In a sample of 2000 males aged 15 to 30, how many would you expect to suffer from anorexia nervosa?

Q3 In a study into how sleeping patterns change with age, a researcher studied the sleep patterns of a group of adults. He found that participants in the 21-30 age range slept for an average of 8.1 hours per night, whilst participants in the 51-60 age range slept for an average of 6.2 hours a night. What was the percentage decrease in the number of hours of sleep from the 21-30 year olds to the 51-60 year olds?

## There's been a 100% increase in my brain power after reading this page...

*Percentages and fractions are really useful, and you need to know about them for your exams. Make sure you can turn a number into a percentage and into a fraction and back again, then put your feet up for five minutes. You've earned it.*

# Estimating

*Estimates* are really handy if you want to get the gist of some data without doing loads of detailed calculations.

## Use *Estimating* to Help You *Understand Data*

A psychologist investigating the relationship between **gender** and **smoking** has shown her results in this table:

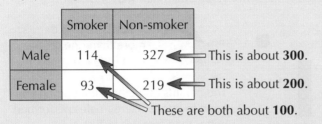

|        | Smoker | Non-smoker |
|--------|--------|------------|
| Male   | 114    | 327        |
| Female | 93     | 219        |

This is about **300**.
This is about **200**.
These are both about **100**.

1) By **estimating**, you can tell roughly what the results show, without doing any tricky calculations.

2) There are **more** male than female **non-smokers**, but **about the same** number of male and female **smokers**.

3) So the table shows that **males** in the study were **more likely** to be non-smokers than **females**.

## *Round* Numbers to *One Significant Figure* to *Estimate*

To **estimate** a calculation:

* Round all of the numbers to **1 significant figure** (see page 4).
* Do the calculation with the **rounded** numbers.

| Participant | Group A | Group B |
|-------------|---------|---------|
| 1           | 2.1     | 1.7     |
| 2           | 3.75    | 3.25    |
| 3           | 2.2     | 1.35    |
| 4           | 1.95    | 1.8     |
| 5           | 5.05    | 2.15    |

### Worked Example

Two groups took a reaction time test. Their scores are shown in the table.

a) **Estimate the mean score for group A.**

b) **Use estimation to find which group had the greater spread of scores.**

**1** *Round the scores for group A to 1 significant figure.*

2, 4, 2, 2, 5

**2** *Find the mean of the rounded scores.*

$2 + 4 + 2 + 2 + 5 = 15$
$15 \div 5 = 3$

The mean score for group A is approximately 3.

*See page 12 for how to work out the mean and range.*

**3** *Round the lowest and highest scores in each group to 1 significant figure.*

Group A
lowest score: $1.95 \approx 2$
highest score: $5.05 \approx 5$

Group B
lowest score: $1.35 \approx 1$
highest score: $3.25 \approx 3$

$\approx$ means 'approximately equal to'

**4** *Use these rounded scores to approximate the range for each group.*

Group A range $\approx 5 - 2 = 3$    Group B range $\approx 3 - 1 = 2$

**5** *Compare the ranges to find the group with the greater spread.*    Group A has the greater spread of scores.

### Practice Question

Q1 Two groups took an aggression test before and after watching a video. Group 1 watched a documentary, and Group 2 watched a boxing match. The test was scored out of 100. The mean scores are shown in the table. Compare the results for Group 1 with the results for Group 2.

*You might want to round to 2 significant figures here.*

|         | Mean test score | |
|---------|--------|-------|
|         | Before | After |
| Group 1 | 45.1   | 46.2  |
| Group 2 | 39.3   | 51.7  |

---

## *I estimate your enjoyment of this page to be about 10 000 000 000 000 000...*

*This stuff is really useful if you want to comment on what some numbers show, but it's too much to do a full calculation. For example, estimating the mean is usually easier than working it out fully. Careful though — if the question asks you to do a specific calculation (e.g. the mean) then an estimate won't get you the marks, you need to do the proper sum.*

# Bar Charts

*First up — **bar charts**. Drawing and understanding them isn't too tricky at all if you know how.*

## Bar Charts Let You **Compare Data** by Looking at the **Bar Heights**

Bar charts are great for presenting data where a variable falls into **categories** (like gender or therapy type) rather than being measured on a numbered scale.　Here's what your average bar chart may look like:

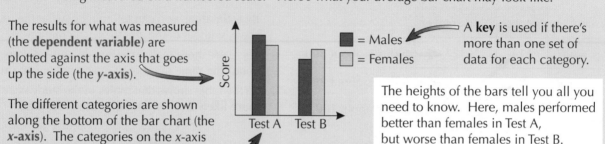

The results for what was measured (the **dependent variable**) are plotted against the axis that goes up the side (the **y-axis**).

The different categories are shown along the bottom of the bar chart (the **x-axis**). The categories on the x-axis are conditions of the **independent variable** (what you're manipulating).

A **key** is used if there's more than one set of data for each category.

The heights of the bars tell you all you need to know. Here, males performed better than females in Test A, but worse than females in Test B.

## Choose a **Sensible Scale** to Make the Best Use of Your Graph Paper

If you need to draw a bar chart from a table of data, here's what you do:

| Group | Average Number of Words Recalled |
|-------|----------------------------------|
| A | 32 |
| B | 16 |
| C | 37 |

These are the categories.

You need to choose a **sensible scale** for your y-axis. The highest number here is 37, so an axis running from 0 to 40 would work nicely.

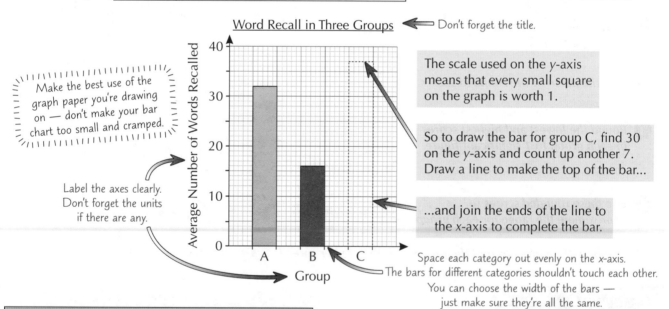

Word Recall in Three Groups ⟵ Don't forget the title.

Make the best use of the graph paper you're drawing on — don't make your bar chart too small and cramped.

Label the axes clearly. Don't forget the units if there are any.

The scale used on the y-axis means that every small square on the graph is worth 1.

So to draw the bar for group C, find 30 on the y-axis and count up another 7. Draw a line to make the top of the bar...

...and join the ends of the line to the x-axis to complete the bar.

Space each category out evenly on the x-axis. The bars for different categories shouldn't touch each other. You can choose the width of the bars — just make sure they're all the same.

## Reading From a Bar Chart is Easy

If you need to **read** from a bar chart, you won't go wrong if you do these things:

1) Work out the scale on the y-axis.
2) Pick the bar you want to read from.
3) Line up a ruler with the **top** of the bar.
4) Read across from the top of the bar to the value on the **y-axis**.

This graph shows that 21% of patients suffered from disorder C.

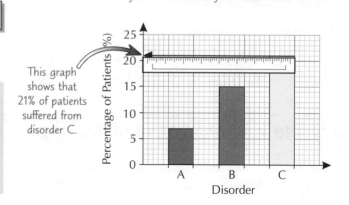

# Bar Charts

### Worked Example 1

A psychologist is researching the effect of five different experimental conditions on reaction time. The graph shows the mean reaction time for the five conditions, for both males and females.

**What is the difference between the mean reaction time for males and females in condition C?**

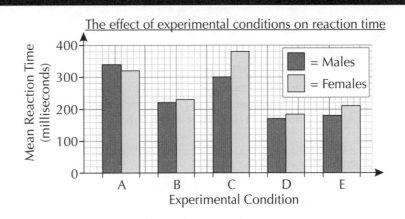

The effect of experimental conditions on reaction time

**1** *Find the bars you need to look at.*

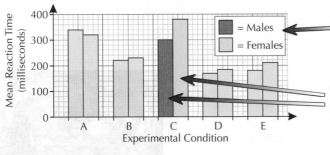

The key tells you that for each category one column shows the number of males and the other column shows the number of females.

These two columns show the results for condition C.

**2** *Read across from the top of the bars to the y-axis.*

The scale on the *y*-axis means that every small square on the graph represents 20 milliseconds.

Pay attention to the scales on graphs and charts — they won't always go up in steps of one.

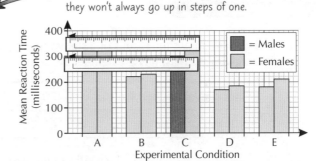

The mean reaction time for females in condition C is **380 milliseconds**.

The mean reaction time for males in condition C is **300 milliseconds**.

**3** *Subtract the smaller value from the larger value to get the difference.*

380 – 300 = **80 milliseconds**

### Worked Example 2

The 'Strange Situation' experiment was carried out in four countries, and children were classed as having a secure attachment, an insecure-avoidant (I-A) attachment or a insecure-resistant (I-R) attachment. The results are shown in the graph on the right.

**What percentage of children in country 2 were classed as having an insecure-avoidant attachment?**

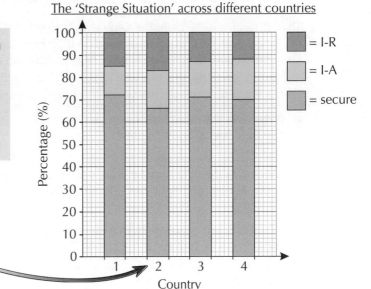

The 'Strange Situation' across different countries

**1** *Find the bar you need to look at.*

The question asks about the people in country 2, so you need to look at the second bar.

# Bar Charts

**2** *Find the section of the bar you need to look at.*

The **height** of each section of the bar represents the percentage of children with that attachment type.

You're interested in the section of the bar that represents the percentage of children classed as having an insecure-avoidant attachment.

**3** *Read across from the top and bottom of the section to the y-axis.*

The scale on the *y*-axis means that every small square on the graph represents **2%**.

The *y*-axis value at the top of the section is **83%**.

The *y*-axis value at the bottom of the section is **66%**.

**4** *Subtract the lower value from the higher value to get the answer.*

83% − 66% = **17%** ← Don't forget to include the % sign in your answer.

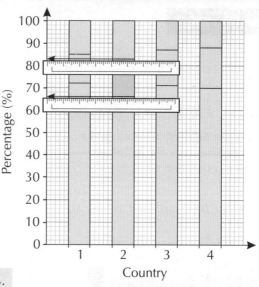

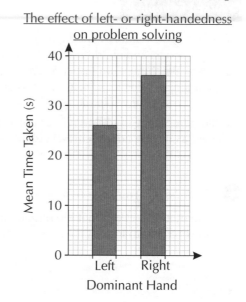

Neil and Sandra's A-Level revision had really taken off since they moved onto bar chats.

## Practice Questions

Q1 The table below shows the results of a study into obedience, where participants were led to believe that they were giving increasingly greater electric shocks to 'learners' each time they made a mistake.

| Shock level reached (volts) | 300 | 330 | 360 | 400 | 450 |
|---|---|---|---|---|---|
| Number of participants | 6 | 2 | 1 | 1 | 18 |

a) Draw a bar chart to display the results of the experiment.

b) Why is a bar chart a suitable way to display these results?

Q2 Aisha did an experiment to investigate whether being left- or right-handed has an effect on problem solving.

All participants were given the same puzzle to solve. They were split into two groups based on their dominant hand. Aisha timed how long it took each person to solve the puzzle.

Her results are in the graph on the right.

a) What was the mean time taken for the right-handed participants?

b) What was the difference between the mean time taken for left- and right-handed participants?

c) What can you conclude from Aisha's experiment by looking at the graph?

The effect of left- or right-handedness on problem solving

# Bar Charts

Q3 The effectiveness of three different drug therapies on two different disorders was tested.
After a month, improvement was assessed by self report, using a scale of 0-20.
A score of 0 means the patient saw no improvement.

The graph below shows the results of the experiment.

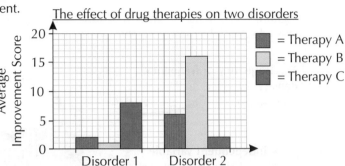

a) What was the most effective therapy for Disorder 1?

b) What was the difference in the average improvement scores for Therapy A for the two disorders?

Q4 Ross conducted a survey about smoking in his town. His results are shown in the table on the right.

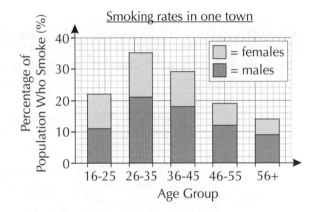

a) What percentage of people aged 46 to 55 are smokers?

b) What percentage of the population are:
   i) male smokers aged 46 or over?
   ii) female smokers aged from 16 to 25?

c) What percentage of people aged 26 to 35 are not smokers?

Q5 Five students took part in a study investigating whether drinking a vitamin drink once a day for 4 weeks helped improve performance on a verbal memory test. The results are shown in the table below.

| Participant | Number of Words Recalled | |
| --- | --- | --- |
| | Before vitamin drink | After vitamin drink |
| 1 | 7 | 19 |
| 2 | 5 | 13 |
| 3 | 8 | 12 |
| 4 | 6 | 21 |
| 5 | 11 | 15 |

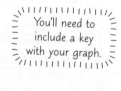

You'll need to include a key with your graph.

Draw a fully labelled bar chart to show the data in the table.
The participants should be labelled along the x-axis.

## Two psychologists walk into a bar...*

*Spotting patterns in a table full of data can be a tricky task. It's a lot easier if you display it in some sort of graph. If your data comes in distinct categories, stick it in a bar chart. It has the added bonus of making results look really pretty.*

*...One says to the other, "Have you met Dr. Pavlov?" The other replies, "I don't recognise the face but the name rings a bell."

# Histograms

*Histograms look a bit like bar charts, but don't be fooled.*

## With **Histograms** it's the **Area** NOT the Height that Matters

Histograms come in useful when you want to display data where both variables fall on a **numbered scale** (like time or height). Here's what one might look like:

The **frequency** or **frequency density** is plotted up the side (the *y*-axis).

The **independent variable** is plotted along the bottom (the *x*-axis).

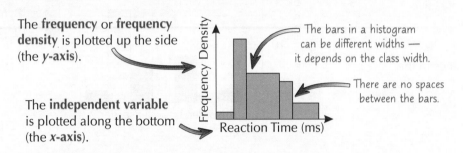

The bars in a histogram can be different widths — it depends on the class width.

There are no spaces between the bars.

Don't be tricked by the taller bars — they won't necessarily show the higher frequencies. It's all about the **area** of the bar. So you need to look at both the height and the width of the bar.

Area = width × height

## **Constructing** a Histogram Involves some **Calculations**

Before drawing a histogram from a table, you need to look at the **class widths**. Here's what to do with them:

1) If the class widths are all the **same**, just pop the **frequency** on the *y*-axis and choose a **suitable scale** for your *x*-axis.

Work out the class width by subtracting the smallest number in each class from the largest number.

This is one class.

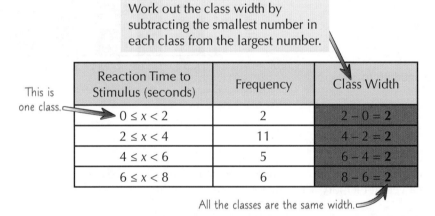

| Reaction Time to Stimulus (seconds) | Frequency | Class Width |
|---|---|---|
| $0 \leq x < 2$ | 2 | $2 - 0 = \mathbf{2}$ |
| $2 \leq x < 4$ | 11 | $4 - 2 = \mathbf{2}$ |
| $4 \leq x < 6$ | 5 | $6 - 4 = \mathbf{2}$ |
| $6 \leq x < 8$ | 6 | $8 - 6 = \mathbf{2}$ |

All the classes are the same width.

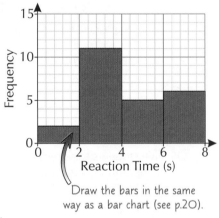

Draw the bars in the same way as a bar chart (see p.20).

2) If the class widths are **different**, you need to work out the **frequency density**. To do that, you use this **formula**:

frequency density = frequency ÷ class width

| Reaction Time to Stimulus (seconds) | Frequency | Class Width | Frequency Density |
|---|---|---|---|
| $0 \leq x < 2$ | 2 | $2 - 0 = \mathbf{2}$ | $2 \div 2 = \mathbf{1}$ |
| $2 \leq x < 5$ | 9 | $5 - 2 = \mathbf{3}$ | $9 \div 3 = \mathbf{3}$ |
| $5 \leq x < 10$ | 10 | $10 - 5 = \mathbf{5}$ | $10 \div 5 = \mathbf{2}$ |
| $10 \leq x < 12$ | 3 | $12 - 10 = \mathbf{2}$ | $3 \div 2 = \mathbf{1.5}$ |

Work out the class widths...

...then work out the frequency density.

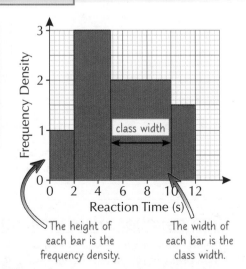

The height of each bar is the frequency density.

The width of each bar is the class width.

# Histograms

## Pay Attention to the *y-axis* When You're **Reading** from a Histogram

If you want to read data off a histogram, have a look at the **y-axis**.
If it shows the **frequency** (because the class widths are all equal), just do these things:

1) Work out the scale on the *y*-axis.

2) Pick the class you want to read from.

3) Read across from the top of the bar to the value on the **y-axis**.

*Like with bar charts, a ruler can help you read across to values on the y-axis.*

14 participants took between 20 s and 30 s to complete the task.

A gap means that there are no results in that class. Here, no participants completed the task between 40 and 50 seconds.

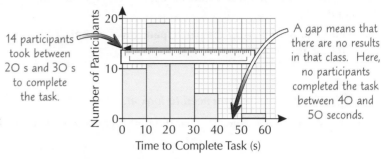

When the *y*-axis shows the **frequency density**, you need the frequency density formula again.
To work out the frequency of a class, just switch the formula around:

$$\text{frequency} = \text{frequency density} \times \text{class width}$$

The frequency for each class is represented by the area of the bar.

*Data with unequal classes is plotted using frequency density because otherwise the heights of the bars would be distorted.*

Class width = 2 – 0 = **2** and frequency density = **1**.
So, frequency = **2 × 1 = 2**.

Class width = 6 – 2 = **4** and frequency density = **1.5**.
So, frequency = **4 × 1.5 = 6**.

Class width = 8 – 6 = **2** and frequency density = **2.5**.
So, frequency = **2 × 2.5 = 5**.

Class width = 12 – 8 = **4** and frequency density = **0.5**.
So, frequency = **4 × 0.5 = 2**.

## The **Shape** of a Histogram Can Tell You Things

The **shape** of a histogram can tell you more about the data. For example:

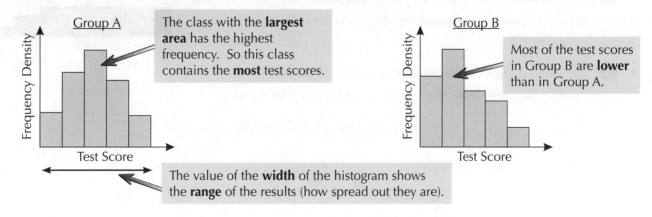

The class with the **largest area** has the highest frequency. So this class contains the **most** test scores.

Most of the test scores in Group B are **lower** than in Group A.

The value of the **width** of the histogram shows the **range** of the results (how spread out they are).

# Histograms

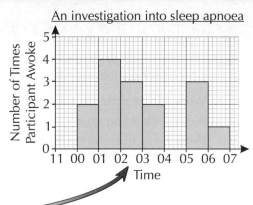

An investigation into sleep apnoea

### Worked Example 1

Some sleep apnoea sufferers visited a sleep laboratory to have their sleep patterns assessed throughout the night. One participant's results are shown in the histogram on the right.

**How many times did the participant wake up between 02:00 and 04:00?**

**1** *Find the classes you need to look at.*

The time between 02:00 and 04:00 is covered by two classes.

**2** *Read across from the top of the bars to the y-axis.*

The y-axis shows the frequency already, so you don't need to do anything with the values.

Between 02:00 and 03:00 the participant woke up **3 times**.

Between 03:00 and 04:00 the participant woke up **2 times**.

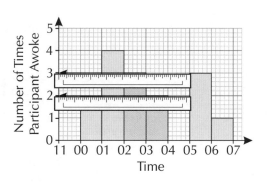

**3** *Add the values together to get the answer.*    $3 + 2 = $ **5 times**

### Worked Example 2

Jason is studying the effect of caffeine on reaction time in a group of students. He recorded the reaction time of each student before and after they received a dose of caffeine, then calculated the percentage improvement. His results are shown in the histogram on the right.

**How many students improved by between 10% and 15%?**

The effect of caffeine on reaction time.

**1** *Find the class you need to look at.*

The percentage improvement between 10 and 15 is covered by just one class.

**2** *Read across from the top of the bar to the y-axis.*

The y-axis shows the **frequency density**, which for this class is **2**.

**3** *Use the frequency density formula to find the frequency.*

Because the y-axis shows the frequency density, you need to use this formula:

$$\text{frequency} = \text{frequency density} \times \text{class width}$$

$2 \times 5 = $ **10 students**

frequency density          class width $(15 - 10 = 5)$

# Histograms

Q1 A psychologist undertook a naturalistic observation to study aggression in a group of children. He recorded the number of aggressive acts made by each child during the course of one hour.

His results for one of the children are shown in the histogram on the right.

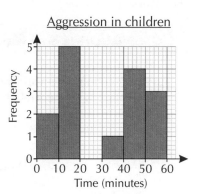
Aggression in children

a) How many more aggressive acts did the child make during the last 10 minutes of the observation compared to the first 10 minutes?

b) What percentage of the total number of aggressive acts were made between 10-20 minutes? Give your answer to the nearest whole number.

Q2 Ivan was investigating the audience effect. He timed how long it took people to solve a mental arithmetic test in the presence of an audience. His results are shown in the table below.

| Time Taken (minutes) | Frequency | Class Width | Frequency Density |
|---|---|---|---|
| $0 \leq x < 2$ | 2 | | |
| $2 \leq x < 5$ | 6 | | |
| $5 \leq x < 10$ | 4 | | |
| $10 \leq x < 15$ | 3 | | |
| $15 \leq x < 25$ | 1 | | |

a) Copy the table and complete the two empty columns.

b) Use your completed table to draw a histogram of Ivan's results. The y-axis should show the frequency density.

Q3 A psychologist was studying the reaction times of males and females to a visual stimulus. The results are shown in the histograms below.

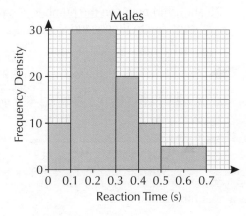
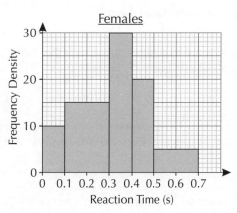

a) How many men had a reaction time of less than 0.4 seconds?

b) What is the total number of females represented in the histogram?

c) Give one conclusion about the reaction times of males and females that can be drawn from the two graphs.

## More bars to draw? You're having a graph...

*Don't let histograms catch you out — before you do anything else, take a good look at the y-axis. If it's showing the frequency density, you've got a bit of calculating to do to work out the frequency before you can write down any answers.*

# Scattergrams and Correlation

*Scattergrams* show the relationship between two variables, like the number of friends you have and the number of chocolate fountains in your house. If there's a relationship, you can say that there's a **correlation**.

## *Correlation is the Measurement of a Relationship*

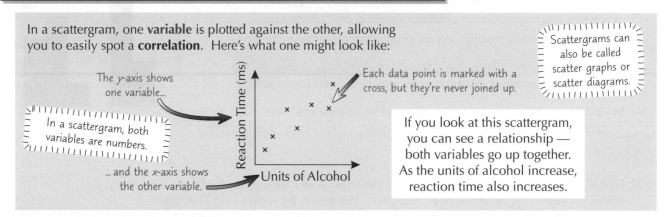

In a scattergram, one **variable** is plotted against the other, allowing you to easily spot a **correlation**. Here's what one might look like:

The *y*-axis shows one variable...

In a scattergram, both variables are numbers.

... and the *x*-axis shows the other variable.

Each data point is marked with a cross, but they're never joined up.

Scattergrams can also be called scatter graphs or scatter diagrams.

If you look at this scattergram, you can see a relationship — both variables go up together. As the units of alcohol increase, reaction time also increases.

## *Plot the Points But Don't Join Them Up*

If you need to **draw** a scattergram from a table full of data, here's what you do:

1) Look at the highest and lowest values for each variable to work out a **scale** for each axis.

The values for this variable range from 3 to 9. A scale from 0 to 10 will do nicely.

| Stress Score | Number of Days Absent due to Illness |
|---|---|
| 4 | 5 |
| 9 | 6 |
| 6 | 10 |
| 4 | 9 |
| 8 | 12 |
| 3 | 3 |

The values for this variable range from 3 to 12. So a scale from 0 to 15 will be nice and neat.

Graph paper tends to be divided into groups of 10 squares. So axes that go up in 1s, 2s, 5s or 10s make data a lot easier to plot.

2) Draw your axes and **label** them.

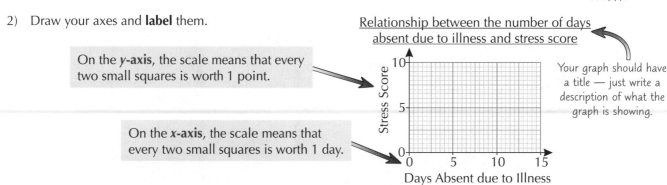

On the *y*-axis, the scale means that every two small squares is worth 1 point.

On the *x*-axis, the scale means that every two small squares is worth 1 day.

Relationship between the number of days absent due to illness and stress score

Your graph should have a title — just write a description of what the graph is showing.

3) Plot each point with a **sharp pencil**. Draw each point as a neat little cross.

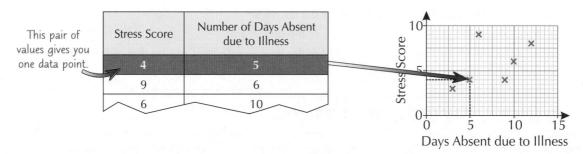

This pair of values gives you one data point.

| Stress Score | Number of Days Absent due to Illness |
|---|---|
| 4 | 5 |
| 9 | 6 |
| 6 | 10 |

*SECTION TWO — GRAPH SKILLS*

# Scattergrams and Correlation

4) On a scattergram, the points are never joined together. However, you may have to draw a **line of best fit**.

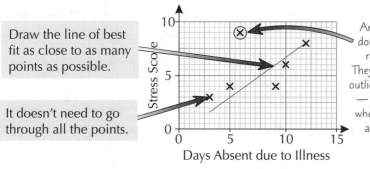

Draw the line of best fit as close to as many points as possible.

It doesn't need to go through all the points.

Anomalous results don't fit in with the rest of the data. They're also known as outliers or rogue scores — just ignore them when you're drawing a line of best fit.

It's surprisingly easy to form a line of get fit...

## There Are **Different Types** of Correlation

If you're interested in the **relationship** between two variables, look at the **correlation**. There are a few different types:

1) **Positive correlation**

This means that as one variable **increases**, the other also **increases**. Likewise, if one **decreases**, the other also **decreases**.

E.g.

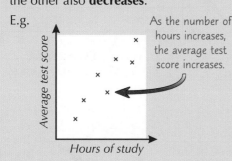

As the number of hours increases, the average test score increases.

2) **Negative correlation**

This means that as one variable **increases**, the other **decreases**.

E.g.

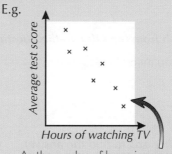

As the number of hours increases, the average test score decreases.

3) **No correlation**

This means that the variables aren't linked — there is no pattern in the data.

E.g.

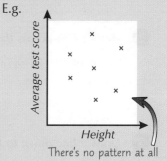

There's no pattern at all to the plotted points here.

The **closer** the points are to the line of best fit, the **stronger** the correlation. A **correlation coefficient** can also be calculated (see pages 46 and 49) and this gives you a numerical value for how **strong** the correlation is. It'll always be a number between –1 and +1, and shows:

• How closely the variables are **linked**.

• The **type** of correlation.

If the coefficient is close to +1 or –1, the variables are **very closely related**.

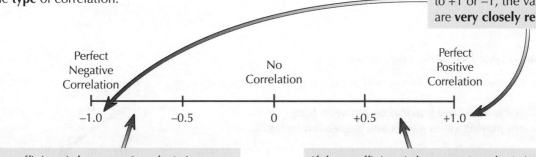

If the coefficient is between 0 and –1, it means that the variables are **negatively correlated**.

If the coefficient is between 0 and +1, it means that the variables are **positively correlated**.

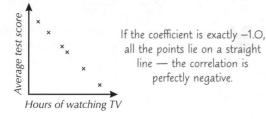

If the coefficient is exactly –1.0, all the points lie on a straight line — the correlation is perfectly negative.

If the coefficient is exactly +1.0, all the points lie on a straight line — the correlation is perfectly positive.

# Scattergrams and Correlation

Relationship between the time spent playing
violent video games and aggression in children

**Worked Example**

Zoë is investigating the relationship between the time spent playing violent video games and aggression levels in children. Her results are shown in the scattergram on the right.

a) **One of the participants received an aggression rating of 8. How many hours per week did they spend playing violent video games?**

b) **Use the scattergram to comment on the relationship between time spent playing violent video games and aggression levels in children.**

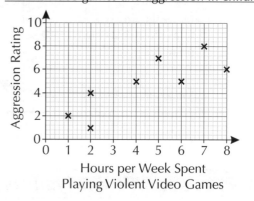

Relationship between the time spent playing violent video games and aggression in children

1️⃣ *For part a), find the axis that you need to look at.*

The variable mentioned in the question is the aggression rating, so you want to look at the *y*-axis.

2️⃣ *Draw a line across the graph from the value in the question.*

Draw the line across until you meet the data point.

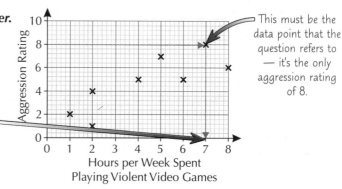

3️⃣ *Draw a line down to the other axis to find the answer.*

Sometimes you might have to read up and across instead.

The participant spent **7 hours** per week playing violent video games.

This must be the data point that the question refers to — it's the only aggression rating of 8.

4️⃣ *For part b), just look at the correlation.*

It's a good idea to draw a line of best fit on the graph to help you.

**There is a positive correlation between time spent playing video games and aggression rating.**

You could also write that as one increases the other also increases.

It's really important to note that you **can't** say something like:

Increasing the time spent playing video games causes an increase in the participant's aggression score.

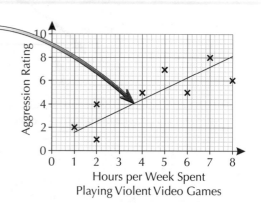

Although there is a positive correlation, there is no way to tell from the graph if one variable actually **causes** the other.

# Scattergrams and Correlation

Q1 Hatim is investigating the relationship between aggression in children and the number of hours spent in day care.

The results of his research are shown in the scattergram on the right.

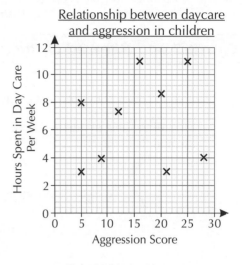

Relationship between daycare and aggression in children

a) How many children are represented by the scattergram?

b) What does the scattergram tell you about the relationship between aggression in children and the number of hours spent in day care? Explain your answer.

Q2 Charlotte is studying the effect of heart rate on people's reaction times. Participants completed a simple reaction test with very loud music playing.

She displayed her results in a scattergram.

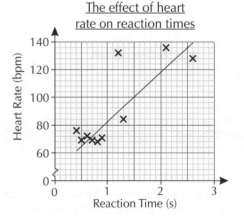

The effect of heart rate on reaction times

a) What type of correlation is shown by the graph?

b) Charlotte identified one anomalous result on her graph. What was that participant's reaction time?

Q3 A psychologist is investigating the effects of day care on social development. She thinks that the longer the children spend in day care, the less time they will spend playing alone.

Her results are shown in the table on the right.

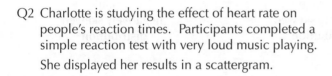
Don't forget to include a title for your graph.

| Child | Hours per Week Spent in Day Care | Average Time Spent Playing Alone (Minutes per Hour) |
|-------|-------|-------|
| A | 30 | 12 |
| B | 10 | 25 |
| C | 5 | 50 |
| D | 15 | 41 |
| E | 32 | 7 |
| F | 5 | 48 |
| G | 35 | 10 |
| H | 7 | 60 |
| I | 12 | 38 |
| J | 2 | 52 |

a) Draw a fully labelled scattergram of the results in the table. Include a line of best fit.

b) Using your line of best fit, predict the time that a child would spend playing alone if they spent 20 hours per week in day care.

c) The correlation coefficient for the data is –0.855. What does this tell you about the relationship between time spent in day care and time spent playing alone?

## *All my relationships seem to go negative pretty fast...*

*An important thing to remember about correlation is that just because there's a relationship between two variables, it doesn't mean that one has a direct effect on the other— it could just be a coincidence. Correlation doesn't mean cause.*

# Distributions

*Distribution describes how data is spread out. It basically tells you whether most of the data is at the higher end, the lower end, or roughly in the middle. **Distribution curves** show this on a graph, and you need to know how they work...*

## *Normal* and *Skewed* Distributions Look Very Different

Distribution curves show how data is **distributed** across the range — they tell you where the most results sit:

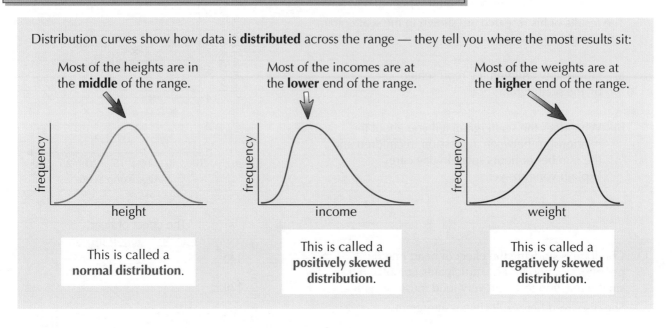

Most of the heights are in the **middle** of the range.

Most of the incomes are at the **lower** end of the range.

Most of the weights are at the **higher** end of the range.

This is called a **normal distribution**.

This is called a **positively skewed distribution**.

This is called a **negatively skewed distribution**.

## *Averages* Tell You *Which Distribution* Your Data Has

Distributions represent the **average** and the **spread** of a set of data.

Once you know the **mean**, **median** and **mode** (see page 12), you can tell which **distribution** your data has. This means you can **sketch** a **distribution curve** for your data.

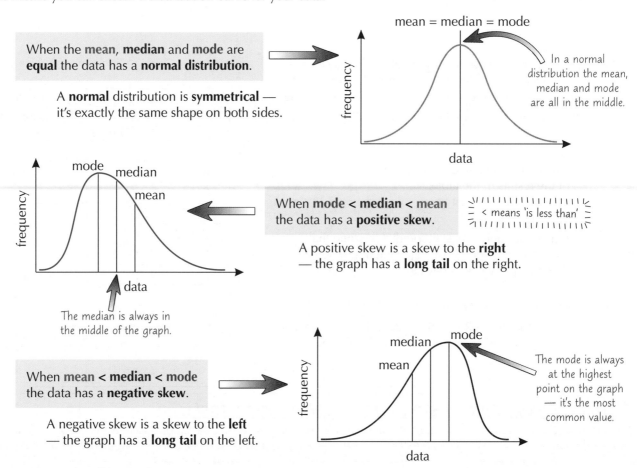

When the **mean**, **median** and **mode** are **equal** the data has a **normal distribution**.

A **normal** distribution is **symmetrical** — it's exactly the same shape on both sides.

mean = median = mode

In a normal distribution the mean, median and mode are all in the middle.

mode median mean

When **mode < median < mean** the data has a **positive skew**.

< means 'is less than'

A positive skew is a skew to the **right** — the graph has a **long tail** on the right.

The median is always in the middle of the graph.

When **mean < median < mode** the data has a **negative skew**.

A negative skew is a skew to the **left** — the graph has a **long tail** on the left.

median mode
mean

The mode is always at the highest point on the graph — it's the most common value.

# Distributions

### Worked Example

Researchers studying stress used a questionnaire to rate participants
on the daily hassles they had experienced in the previous week.

The mean daily hassles score was 65, the median daily hassles score was 67,
and the mode daily hassles score was 78.

**Sketch a graph to show the likely distribution curve for the scores in this study.**

**1** *Use the mean, median and mode to work out which distribution the data has.*

When mean < median < mode, the data has a negative skew.

mean = 65 < median = 67 < mode = 78
So the data has a **negative skew**.

**2** *Draw some axes and label them.*

The axis pointing up on a distribution curve is always **frequency**.
The axis pointing across is labelled with what your graph is showing
— here it's **score** on a daily hassles questionnaire.

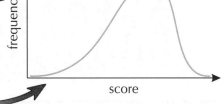

**3** *Sketch the distribution.*

Negatively skewed distributions have a long tail on the left.

**4** *Mark the mode at the highest point of the graph.*

The mode is always at the highest point of a distribution curve.

**5** *Mark the median in the middle of the graph.*

The median is always in the middle.

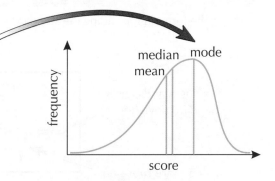

**6** *Mark the mean to the left of the median.*

You know that mean < median < mode,
so the mean must be on the left of the graph.

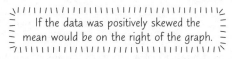
If the data was positively skewed the
mean would be on the right of the graph.

### Practice Questions

Q1 200 participants filled in a questionnaire used to find aggression ratings. The mean aggression score was 29,
the median aggression score was 20, and the mode aggression score was 19.

a) Sketch a graph showing the most likely distribution curve for the results of this questionnaire.

b) What type of distribution is shown on your graph?

Q2 Participants in a memory study were tested on their recall of a list of 15 words.
The mean number of words recalled was 10, the median was 11, and the mode was 13.
What type of distribution does this data have?

Q3 Anna is studying the relationship between IQ and gender roles. She gives 25 participants an IQ test.
The participants' scores are normally distributed. Sketch a distribution curve of Anna's results.

---

## *I don't want to put a negative skew on this...*

*...but I'm afraid you need to learn all this stuff. The key things to remember are what each of the distributions look like,
and which order the mean, median and mode are in for each one. If it's still baffling you, go back through these pages.*

# Standard Deviation

*Like the range (see page 12), the **standard deviation** describes how spread out a group of numbers are.*

## The **Standard Deviation** Measures **Spread** from the **Middle**

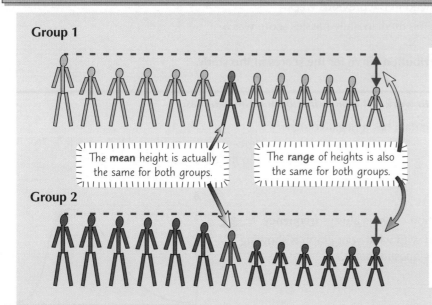

**Group 1**

The **mean** height is actually the same for both groups.

The **range** of heights is also the same for both groups.

**Group 2**

In Group 1, there are **lots of men roughly in the middle**, and one tall man and one short man.

In Group 2, you've got loads of men at the taller end, and loads at the shorter end but **fewer in the middle**.

The heights are **less consistent** in Group 2 than Group 1 — they **deviate more from the mean**. So it can be said that Group 2 has a **greater** standard deviation than Group 1.

## Find the **Standard Deviation** Using the **Formula**

This is the formula for finding the standard deviation:

This symbol is **sigma** — it means 'sum of'.

'*s*' just stands for standard deviation.

$$s = \sqrt{\frac{\sum (x - \bar{x})^2}{n - 1}}$$

'*x*' stands for a value in the data set, and '$\bar{x}$' is the **mean**.
So '$(x - \bar{x})^2$' means "take away the mean from the value, then square the result."

**Square root** sign

'*n*' stands for the number of values.

So, to find the standard deviation of a group of values:

If you have a calculation with lots of stages like this, don't round your answer until the very end.

1) Work out the mean of all the values.
2) Find $(x - \bar{x})^2$ for each value.
3) Add these numbers together and divide the total by the number of values minus one.
4) Take the square root of your answer.

## The **Standard Deviation** Can Help You to **Understand** Your **Results**

1) Standard deviation is a **better measure** of spread than the **range** because it is less affected by **extreme values**. But it takes a lot longer to calculate.

2) You can **compare** the standard deviation of two or more groups to help you to make conclusions.

|       | Score |                    |
|-------|-------|--------------------|
|       | Mean  | Standard Deviation |
| Boys  | 56    | 4.2                |
| Girls | 64    | 6.7                |

In this table, the girls' **average score** was higher than the boys', but their **standard deviation** was also higher.

**Although girls scored more highly than boys, they were also less consistent.**

# Standard Deviation

### Worked Example

Zainab studied the body's reaction to mild stress by measuring five people's heart rates whilst they were stuck in a traffic jam. Her results are shown in the table on the right. **Calculate the standard deviation of Zainab's results.**

| Participant | Heart rate (bpm) |
|---|---|
| A | 75 |
| B | 81 |
| C | 73 |
| D | 77 |
| E | 68 |

**1** *Write out the equation.*

$$s = \sqrt{\dfrac{\sum (x - \bar{x})^2}{n - 1}}$$

**2** *Work out the mean heart rate, $\bar{x}$.*     $(73 + 81 + 75 + 68 + 77) \div 5 = \textbf{74.8 bpm}$

*If you can't remember how to find the mean, see page 12.*

**3** *Work out $(x - \bar{x})^2$ for each value of x.*

For each heart rate in the table, you need to take away the mean, then square the answer.

A:  *x* is 75.     $(75 - 74.8)^2 = 0.2^2 = \textbf{0.04}$
B:  *x* is 81.     $(81 - 74.8)^2 = 6.2^2 = \textbf{38.44}$
C:  *x* is 73.     $(73 - 74.8)^2 = (-1.8)^2 = \textbf{3.24}$
D:  *x* is 77.     $(77 - 74.8)^2 = 2.2^2 = \textbf{4.84}$
E:  *x* is 68.     $(68 - 74.8)^2 = (-6.8)^2 = \textbf{46.24}$

*If you square a negative number, the answer is always positive.*

Tiddles wasn't your standard Father Christmas, but he was filling the role with panache.

**4** *Add up all these numbers to find $\sum(x - \bar{x})^2$.*

$0.04 + 38.44 + 3.24 + 4.84 + 46.24 = \textbf{92.8}$

**5** *Divide this number by the number of values minus 1 (n − 1), then take the square root to get the answer.*

*Be careful with your units. The standard deviation will be in the same units as your data.*

$92.8 \div (5 - 1) = 23.2$
$\sqrt{23.2} = \textbf{4.82 bpm to 3 s.f.}$

*Round your answer to a sensible level, rather than writing a long string of decimal places.*

### Practice Questions

Q1 Five people took part in a memory experiment. The number of words they could recall was recorded.
Their scores were 5, 15, 10, 11 and 9, giving a mean score of 10.
Calculate the standard deviation of their scores, giving the answer to 3 significant figures.

Q2 The results for an experiment are shown in the table on the right. Calculate the standard deviation of the time in seconds, to 2 significant figures.

| Participant | A | B | C | D | E | F |
|---|---|---|---|---|---|---|
| Time (s) | 12 | 33 | 18 | 27 | 14 | 16 |

Q3 A researcher was studying how many hours of television people of different ages watched each week. His results are shown in the table on the right. Comment on his results.

| | Age (years) | 16 – 20 | 21 – 25 | 26 – 30 |
|---|---|---|---|---|
| Amount of television watched per week (hours) | Mean | 15 | 8 | 8 |
| | Standard deviation | 2.3 | 4.1 | 2.2 |

## Deviate from the mean — be nice for once...

*It's a bit of a mission to find the standard deviation, I'll grant you, but luckily there's a formula to help you out. You might have to work out the mean of the data yourself, but apart from that, it's just about plugging the numbers into the right places. So, time to whip out those calculators, sharpen those pencils and start deviating all over the place...*

# Writing Hypotheses

*Before you can test your results, you need to know what your hypothesis is...*

## A **Hypothesis** is a **Statement** That Predicts **What Will Happen**

You might be investigating how much sleep adults get compared to children.

There are three possibilities for the results:

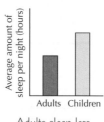

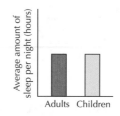

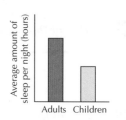

Adults sleep less than children.

Adults and children sleep the same amount.

Adults sleep more than children.

Before you start your research you need to make a **hypothesis** abut how you think sleep differs between adults and children. This is called an **alternative hypothesis**.

You might make a hypothesis with a **direction**...

"Adults sleep less than children" is a **directional hypothesis**. It says that adults and children will get different amounts of sleep, and that adults will get less.

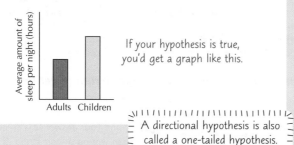

If your hypothesis is true, you'd get a graph like this.

A directional hypothesis is also called a one-tailed hypothesis.

...or you might make one **without** direction.

"Adults and children sleep different amounts" is a **non-directional hypothesis**. It says that adults and children will get different amounts of sleep, but it doesn't say who will get more.

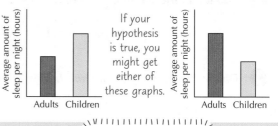

If your hypothesis is true, you might get either of these graphs.

A non-directional hypothesis is also called a two-tailed hypothesis.

You also need to write a **null hypothesis**.

The null hypothesis is that there will be **no significant difference** between the things you are measuring (or no correlation if your alternative hypothesis is that two variables are correlated, see pages 28-29). In this example:

For both the alternative hypotheses above, the null hypothesis is "there is no significant difference in the average amount of sleep per night between adults and children".

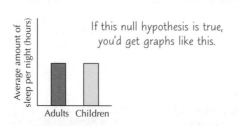

If this null hypothesis is true, you'd get graphs like this.

During research, **you assume the null hypothesis is true**, and do experiments or collect data to try and **disprove the null hypothesis**.

If you get results that force you to reject your null hypothesis, then your data **supports your alternative hypothesis**.

# Writing Hypotheses

## Figure Out Your Hypothesis *Before You Start*

**Before you start** an investigation, you need to:

1) Come up with an **alternative hypothesis** about what might happen.
   This is sometimes called the **experimental hypothesis** if it's about data you're collecting from an experiment.

2) Figure out whether this hypothesis is:

   - **Directional** (it says how you expect something to change in your investigation).

   - **Non-directional** (it just says you expect something to change, but not how you expect it to change).

3) Identify your **null hypothesis** — what you would expect to happen if there's nothing going on.

> You also should be able to **work out** from a description of an investigation whether the alternative hypothesis is **directional** or **non-directional**, and what the **null hypothesis** is. This is important if you are doing **statistics** on **someone else's data**.

### Worked Example

Martha is investigating how reading women's magazines affects women's self-esteem. She hypothesises that women who read more magazines will have lower self-esteem than women who read fewer magazines.
**Is this a directional or non-directional hypothesis?  What is her null hypothesis?**

**1** *Decide whether the hypothesis says how Martha expects women's self-esteem to differ depending on how many magazines they read.*

Martha thinks women who read **more** magazines will have **lower** self-esteem, so she has said how she thinks women's self-esteem will change. This means her alternative hypothesis is **directional**.

**2** *Identify the null hypothesis.*
The null hypothesis is always that there's nothing going on. In this case, it means that there will be no difference in women's self-esteem, whether they read more or fewer magazines.

A suitable null hypothesis would be:
**"There will be no significant difference in women's self esteem depending on the number of women's magazines they read"**.

## Practice Questions

Q1 A researcher is investigating the relationship between the seasons and the incidence of depression. He hypothesises that rates of depression increase with decreasing day length.
   a) Is this hypothesis directional or non-directional?
   b) What should the researcher's null hypothesis be?

Q2 Richard is investigating whether playing violent computer games increases the frequency of violent behaviour.
   a) Give a directional alternative hypothesis he could use and its null hypothesis.
   b) Give a non-directional alternative hypothesis he could use and its null hypothesis.

---

## *What do you call a hypothesis about a large, grey animal from Africa...*

*This stuff is a bit of a headache, but it's an essential part of how science works and it's vital that you understand it if you want to be able to use the statistical tests in the rest of this section. So take a deep breath, and read it again.*

# Levels of Significance

*Once you've got your data, you need to see whether or not it backs up your null hypothesis.*
*The key thing here is comparing the results to what you would expect to see by chance...*

## Statistics is All About **Probability**

Think about tossing a coin:
Each time you toss the coin, you are as likely to get 'heads' as 'tails'.

| Tally | |
|---|---|
| Heads | JHT JHT IIII |
| Tails | JHT JHT I |

If you keep tossing the coin over and over, you probably won't get exactly the same number of heads and tails, but the numbers should always be quite **similar**.

If the number of heads and tails gets too different, you'd think it was **unlikely** to just be down to chance and that the coin was biased.

| Tally | |
|---|---|
| Heads | JHT JHT JHT JHT JHT JHT III |
| Tails | JHT JHT JHT II |

In the same way, when scientists test hypotheses, they find out how likely it is that their results are just due to chance. If it looks like it's too unlikely that their results are caused by chance, they **reject the null hypothesis** and say their data supports the **alternative hypothesis**.

It's all about **probability**, so here's a quick recap before getting down to the details:

Probabilities can be written **as a number** from 0-1...
- 0 means something is **impossible**.
- 1 means something is **certain**.
- 0.05 means something will happen **5 times in 100**.

... and can also be written as **percentages**:
- 0% means something is **impossible**.
- 100% means it's **certain**.
- 5% means something will happen **5 times in 100**.

## *Test* Your Results Against *Chance* to See if They're *Significant*

1) Once you've sorted out your hypotheses (see p.36-37), you need to choose a **significance level** — this is the 'level of proof' you're looking for before you'll read anything into your results. Significance levels are always very small probabilities, usually 5% or less.

> Normally they're written as $p \leq 0.05$ or $p \leq 0.01$.
> $p$ stands for probability, and $\leq$ means 'less than or equal to'.

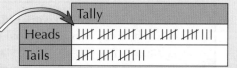
*The smaller the significance level, the stronger the evidence you're looking for that your results aren't just due to chance.*

2) Statistical tests turn all your results into a single **test statistic**. You then just have to find out **how likely** getting this test statistic is if the null hypothesis is actually true.

3) If the probability of getting your results is **less** than the significance level, then they are **really unlikely** to have happened by chance. This means your results **support the alternative hypothesis** being true rather than the null hypothesis, and you can **reject the null hypothesis** as an explanation for your results.

4) When you can reject the null hypothesis, you can say the result is **significant**.

5) If your data has a probability **greater** than 0.05 (or 0.01 if you set a really small significance level), unfortunately you've shown nothing. However, not getting a significant result doesn't necessarily mean the null hypothesis is true.

*The idea is that if you set your significance level to be very small, events with a probability equal to or smaller than the significance level are really unlikely to happen by chance.*

> $p \leq 0.05$ (5%) is ok for most tests. If you want really strong evidence that the null hypothesis is untrue before you reject it, then you could go for $p \leq 0.01$ (1%).

# Levels of Significance

## A *Significant Result* Could Still be Down to *Chance*

- If data passes a test at the 0.05 level, it means there is up to a **5% chance** of the results having happened at **random**. So 5% of the time, a significant result will just be **due to chance**.
- This is part of why scientists **repeat** each other's work — if a lot of people get the **same result** testing the same thing then it's **less likely** to be a fluke.

### Worked Example

A researcher is investigating whether a new mental exercise improves memory. He collects data on the memory performance of a group of people who have been regularly doing the exercise and on the performance of a group of people who have not been doing the exercise. He compares the data from the two groups using a statistical test and finds his results have a probability of 0.03.

**a) Are his results significant at the 0.05 level?  If he was testing the data at this level what should he conclude?**

**b) Are his results significant at the 0.01 level? If he was testing the data at this level what should he conclude?**

**1** *Identify the null and alternative hypotheses.*

> Alternative hypothesis: **There is a significant relationship between increased exercise and memory.**
> Null hypothesis: **There is no relationship between increased exercise and memory.**

**2** *Compare the probability of his results to 0.05.*

1) 0.03 is **less** than 0.05.
2) His results are less than 5% likely to have happened by chance.
3) So his results **are significant** at the 0.05 level.

> Conclusion:
> **The results support the hypothesis that the exercise improves memory.**

*If the result is significant you can reject the null hypothesis. Your results support the alternative hypothesis.*

Harold and Greta celebrated their significant results the only way they knew how.

**3** *Compare the probability of his results to 0.01.*

1) 0.03 is **more** than 0.01.
2) His results are more than 1% likely to have happened by chance.
3) So his results **are not significant** at the 0.01 level.

*This is why you should consider your significance level before you start — it can have a big effect on your conclusion.*

> Conclusion:
> **The results do not support the hypothesis that the exercise improves people's memory.**

## Practice Question

Q1 A specialist in anomalous experience is testing the alternative hypothesis that a psychic is better than chance at guessing a letter written on a piece of paper. He tests his data using a significance level of 0.05, and after a statistical analysis gets a probability of 0.5.

a) Are his results significant?

b) What should his conclusion be?

---

## *I'm significantly more tired now than when I started this page...*

*Understanding a little bit about probability is really important. The next chunk of this book is all about various statistical tests, so you won't get very far if you don't understand what the results mean. It's time to knuckle down, I'm afraid.*

# The Sign Test

*This is it. The moment you've been waiting for. The first statistical test — the sign test. This is the only test you could be asked to actually do in the exam, so make sure you read these pages really carefully. It's really not that bad. Honest.*

## The **Sign Test** Tells You if There's a **Difference** Between **Two** Sets of Scores

Ten people suffering from anxiety were asked to rate their anxiety level before and after trialling a new anxiety drug. They rated their anxiety level on a 7-point scale (7 = highly anxious, 1 = not at all anxious.)

If there was **no difference** in anxiety level before and after taking the drug, you'd expect results like this:

| Participant | 1 | 2 | 3 | 4 | 5 | 6 | 7 | 8 | 9 | 10 |
|---|---|---|---|---|---|---|---|---|---|---|
| Anxiety Level (1-7) Before drug | 6 | 5 | 7 | 3 | 4 | 2 | 5 | 6 | 7 | 4 |
| After drug | 6 | 5 | 7 | 3 | 4 | 2 | 5 | 6 | 7 | 4 |

All the numbers in the table are the same — each person had the same anxiety level before and after trialling the drug.

| Participant | 1 | 2 | 3 | 4 | 5 | 6 | 7 | 8 | 9 | 10 |
|---|---|---|---|---|---|---|---|---|---|---|
| Anxiety Level (1-7) Before drug | 7 | 7 | 7 | 7 | 7 | 7 | 7 | 7 | 7 | 7 |
| After drug | 1 | 1 | 1 | 1 | 1 | 1 | 1 | 1 | 1 | 1 |

If there was a **really big difference** in the ratings, you'd expect more dramatic results like this:

Participants were all highly anxious before trialling the drug...

... but showed a large reduction in anxiety after trialling the drug.

Often, your results **won't** be that extreme. They may look something more like this:

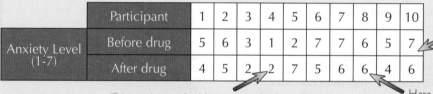

| Participant | 1 | 2 | 3 | 4 | 5 | 6 | 7 | 8 | 9 | 10 |
|---|---|---|---|---|---|---|---|---|---|---|
| Anxiety Level (1-7) Before drug | 5 | 6 | 3 | 1 | 2 | 7 | 7 | 6 | 5 | 7 |
| After drug | 4 | 5 | 2 | 2 | 7 | 5 | 6 | 6 | 4 | 6 |

This person had high anxiety levels before and after trialling the drug.

This participant had low anxiety levels before and after trialling the drug.

Here, the person had the same anxiety levels before and after.

The sign test would **compare** the sets of data to see if there's a significant difference between the **two sets of scores**, or whether any difference is just down to chance.

## The **Sign Test** Uses **Nominal** Data

The sign test isn't that tricky to use. (Honest.) But, before you start, you'll need to make sure that...

1) You get **two sets** of data from **each participant**.  
*This is called a repeated measures design.*

2) Or... each set of data comes from **matched participants** who have been paired together based on characteristics such as age, gender, etc.  
*This is called a matched pairs design.*

3) The data scores are compared and changed into categories (i.e. the **difference** between them is either **positive** or **negative**).  
*The data changes from ordinal to nominal (see page 64).*

# The Sign Test

## The *Sign Test* Can Tell You if Your Results are *Significant*

To do a sign test:

1) Work out the **observed value** for your data — see below for how to do this.

2) Find *N* — this is just the number of differences you've calculated.

3) Compare your observed value with the **critical value** in the right critical values table.

| | Level of significance for two-tailed test | | | |
|---|---|---|---|---|
| | *0.10* | *0.05* | *0.02* | *0.01* |
| | Level of significance for one-tailed test | | | |
| *N* | *0.05* | *0.025* | *0.01* | *0.005* |
| 5 | 0 | — | — | — |
| 6 | 0 | 0 | — | — |
| 7 | 0 | 0 | 0 | — |
| 8 | 1 | 0 | 0 | 0 |
| 9 | 1 | 1 | 0 | 0 |
| 10 | 1 | 1 | 0 | 0 |
| 11 | 2 | 1 | 1 | 0 |

A critical values table is a list of values to compare your observed value against, to tell you whether it is significant at different levels of significance. For some tests, a result is significant if your observed value is equal to or greater than the critical value. For other tests, a result is significant if your observed value is equal to or less than the critical value.

Read down the column at the level of significance you're after.

Find your value of *N* here.

The point where they cross is your critical value. Here, it's 1.

4) If your observed value is **less than or equal to** the critical value, then you have a **significant** result and can **reject the null hypothesis**.

### Worked Example

A researcher asked participants to rate how happy they felt before and after watching an uplifting film. (1 = very happy, 8 = sad.) She hypothesises that:

**Participants will be significantly happier after watching an uplifting film than before.**

| Participant | 1 | 2 | 3 | 4 | 5 | 6 | 7 | 8 | 9 |
|---|---|---|---|---|---|---|---|---|---|
| Happiness Level (1-8) Before film | 5 | 4 | 3 | 2 | 7 | 5 | 4 | 4 | 7 |
| After film | 6 | 7 | 1 | 8 | 8 | 7 | 6 | 4 | 6 |

**1** **Work out the difference between each participant's two scores.**

It's a good idea to do this in a table. Add **two** extra rows to the bottom of the table — one for the **number** and one for the **sign**.

| | Participant | 1 | 2 | 3 | 4 | 5 | 6 | 7 | 8 | 9 |
|---|---|---|---|---|---|---|---|---|---|---|
| Happiness Level (1-8) | Before film | 5 | 4 | 3 | 2 | 7 | 5 | 4 | 4 | 7 |
| | After film | 6 | 7 | 1 | 8 | 8 | 7 | 6 | 4 | 6 |
| | Difference | 1 | 3 | 2 | 6 | 1 | 2 | 2 | 0 | 1 |
| | Sign (+/−) | + | + | − | + | + | + | + | | − |

Always subtract in the same direction to see if the result is positive or negative. Remove any differences of zero from the results.

**2** **Add up the number of positive and negative signs. The smallest total is the observed value.**

| | Participant | 1 | 2 | 3 | 4 | 5 | 6 | 7 | 8 | 9 |
|---|---|---|---|---|---|---|---|---|---|---|
| Happiness Level (1-8) | Before film | 5 | 4 | 3 | 2 | 7 | 5 | 4 | 4 | 7 |
| | After film | 6 | 7 | 1 | 8 | 8 | 7 | 6 | 4 | 6 |
| | Difference | 1 | 3 | 2 | 6 | 1 | 2 | 2 | 0 | 1 |
| | Sign (+/−) | + | + | − | + | + | + | + | | − |

Positive signs: 6
Negative signs: 2

You can ignore any results where the difference is 0.

2 is smaller than 6, so the observed value is **2**.

# The Sign Test

**3** *Use a critical values table to find out if your result is significant.*

1) You need to know the number of participants, *N* — in this study it's 8.

*N is 8, not 9, because one participant was removed.*

2) The hypothesis was **directional**, so use the **one-tailed test**.

3) Use a **significance level** of 0.05 if you're not told otherwise.

*This is the column for a one-tailed test with a p of 0.05.*

The critical value is **1**.

*This is the row for N = 8.*

The observed value, 2, is **more than** the critical value. So the results **are not significant**.

**There was no significant difference in ratings of happiness before and after watching an uplifting film.**

| Level of significance for two-tailed test | | | |
|---|---|---|---|
| **0.10** | **0.05** | **0.02** | **0.01** |
| Level of significance for one-tailed test | | | |
| ***N*** **0.05** | **0.025** | **0.01** | **0.005** |
| 5   0 | — | — | — |
| 6   0 | 0 | — | — |
| 7   0 | 0 | 0 | — |
| 8   1 | 0 | 0 | 0 |
| 9   1 | 1 | 0 | 0 |
| 10   1 | 1 | 0 | 0 |
| 11   2 | 1 | 1 | 0 |

## Practice Questions

**Q1** A psychologist compares how many hours of sleep 8 participants had on a Friday night one week, with how many hours of sleep they had on a Sunday night during the same week.

a) He marks the difference between each participant's set of scores as either positive or negative. What type of data does he now have?

b) Given that none of the participants had a difference of zero, what is the value of *N* for this data set?

**Q2** Find the critical value that you would use for the following sign tests. (Assume there are no differences of 0 in the results.)

*Use the critical values table above.*

a) A two-tailed test with an *N* of 9 at the 1% level.

b) A one-tailed test with an *N* of 11, using $p \leq 0.05$.

**Q3** A researcher believes that students in Year 12 will read significantly more books over one year than students in Year 13. In her study, students are matched by gender and GCSE results. Her results are shown in the table on the right.

| Participant | 1 | 2 | 3 | 4 | 5 | 6 |
|---|---|---|---|---|---|---|
| Number of books read — Year 12 | 2 | 3 | 5 | 6 | 7 | 5 |
| Number of books read — Year 13 | 4 | 2 | 2 | 5 | 6 | 8 |

a) Explain why the researcher could use a sign test to analyse her results.

b) What is the null hypothesis of this research?

**Q4** A psychologist hypothesised that the time of day affects memory. She asked participants to learn and recall a list of ten words in the morning, and again in the evening. Her results are shown in the table below.

| Participant | 1 | 2 | 3 | 4 | 5 | 6 | 7 | 8 | 9 | 10 | 11 | 12 |
|---|---|---|---|---|---|---|---|---|---|---|---|---|
| Number of words recalled — Morning | 2 | 3 | 8 | 6 | 7 | 9 | 10 | 3 | 9 | 8 | 9 | 10 |
| Number of words recalled — Evening | 6 | 3 | 5 | 4 | 6 | 9 | 10 | 2 | 7 | 10 | 10 | 6 |

a) Is the alternative hypothesis directional or non-directional?

b) What is the value of *N* for this data set?

c) Use the critical values table above to find the critical value for this data at the 5% level.

d) Are these results significant, for $p \leq 0.05$?

---

## *I'm sure that dream about statistical testing was definitely a sign...*

*Knowing all about the sign test will make your life complete. Sort of. It'll at least help you pass your exams, and that's something for a start. In actual fact though, the sign test is really straightforward. Subtract each participant's scores from each other, then count up how many differences are positive and how many are negative. See... it's OK really.*

# Wilcoxon Test

*Here's another test to dig your teeth into. There's a lot to learn, so take it steady...*

## Use the **Wilcoxon Test** if the **Same People** are in **Both Groups**

A researcher wants to know if taking a motivational course helps people to decrease the number of cigarettes they smoke.

He records the average number of cigarettes each of 8 smokers smoked per day the week before the course, and the week after the course.

BEFORE:
AFTER:

BEFORE:
AFTER:

BEFORE:
AFTER:

BEFORE:
AFTER:

*This person smoked 4 cigarettes per day before the course and 2 after.*

*These people smoked more cigarettes per day after the course than before it.*

BEFORE:
AFTER:

BEFORE:
AFTER:

BEFORE:
AFTER:

BEFORE:
AFTER:

*This person smoked the same number of cigarettes per day before and after the course.*

Just looking at the numbers, it's **hard to tell** whether people generally smoked fewer cigarettes after the motivational course than they did before it.

The **Wilcoxon test** can tell you whether results like this are **significant**. Here, it'd tell you whether there's a significant difference in the number of cigarettes people smoked before the motivational course compared to after the motivational course.

## The Wilcoxon Test is Only for **Paired Data**

If you want to use the Wilcoxon test, you need to make sure you have...

1) Data from **two different conditions** that can be put in **order of size**.

2) Data that comes in **pairs**, either because the **same participants** took part in **both conditions** (a repeated measures design) or because the participants are **matched up** (a matched pairs design). You need to know which pairs of data go together though — the answer would be wrong if they got jumbled up.

*This test works for ordinal or interval data (see page 64).*

*The data for this test isn't independent — it comes in pairs.*

## Use the **Critical Values Table** to See if There is a **Difference Between Groups**

**A Wilcoxon test** will give an observed value, called *T*. Once you've got *T*, look at the critical values table to see if your results are significant.

1) Look up your **sample size** and **significance level** in a critical values table. The sample size, *N*, is the **number of differences** calculated from the participants. But don't include any differences of zero.

2) If *T* is **equal to or less than** the **critical value**, your result is significant, and you can **reject the null hypothesis**.

# Wilcoxon Test

**Worked Example**

A researcher wanted to test the hypothesis that attending a motivational course would decrease the number of cigarettes that smokers smoked in a day. He collected data on how many cigarettes 8 smokers smoked on average in the week before attending a motivational course and in the week after attending the course. His results are shown in the table below. On conducting a Wilcoxon test, he calculated an observed value of $T = 4$.

**Did smokers significantly reduce their smoking in the week following the course? Use a significance level of 0.05.**

| Participant | 1 | 2 | 3 | 4 | 5 | 6 | 7 | 8 |
|---|---|---|---|---|---|---|---|---|
| Cigarettes smoked per day before the course | 4 | 10 | 3 | 5 | 10 | 3 | 4 | 2 |
| Cigarettes smoked per day after the course | 2 | 5 | 1 | 6 | 10 | 0 | 3 | 3 |

**1** *Find the number of participants in your study.*

1) One participant smokes the same number of cigarettes per day **before** and **after** the course.

2) This means their difference is **zero**, so their results are **removed**.   $N = 7$

3) There are 8 participants to start with, so $N = 8 - 1 = 7$.

**2** *Decide if the hypothesis was directional or non-directional.*

The hypothesis was **directional**, so use the **one-tailed test**.

*The hypothesis predicted how smoking behaviour would change as a result of a motivational course. This makes it directional.*

**3** *Use a critical values table to find out if your result is significant.*

The significance level you're interested in is 0.05.

This is the column for a one-tailed test with a $p$ of 0.05.

This is the row for $N = 7$

The critical value of $T$ is **3**.

The observed value $T = 4$ is **greater than** 3 so the results are **not significant**.

**Smokers did not smoke significantly fewer cigarettes per day in the week after the motivational course than in the week before.**

| | Level of significance for two-tailed test | | | |
|---|---|---|---|---|
| | **0.10** | **0.05** | **0.02** | **0.01** |
| | Level of significance for one-tailed test | | | |
| **N** | **0.05** | **0.025** | **0.01** | **0.005** |
| 5 | 0 | | | |
| 6 | 2 | 0 | | |
| 7 | 3 | 2 | 0 | |
| 8 | 5 | 3 | 1 | 0 |
| 9 | 8 | 5 | 3 | 1 |
| 10 | 10 | 8 | 5 | 3 |
| 11 | 13 | 10 | 7 | 5 |
| 12 | 17 | 13 | 9 | 7 |
| 13 | 21 | 17 | 12 | 9 |

## Practice Questions

Q1 Find the critical value of $T$ for the following Wilcoxon tests (assume there are no differences of 0 in the results).

*Use the critical values table above.*

a) A one-tailed test with an $N$ of 10 at the 0.05 level.

b) A two-tailed test with an $N$ of 12 at the 1% level.

c) A one-tailed test with 8 participants, tested at the 0.01 level.

d) A two-tailed test with 11 participants, using $p \leq 0.01$.

# Wilcoxon Test

Q2 A scientist is studying the relationship between sleep apneoea and BMI. He measures the BMI of 7 randomly selected people who suffer from sleep apnoea and 7 people who do not. His results are shown in the table below.

| | BMI | | | | | | |
|---|---|---|---|---|---|---|---|
| Suffers from sleep apnoea | 32.2 | 29.4 | 31.2 | 28.5 | 26.4 | 33.3 | 31.9 |
| Does not suffer from sleep apnoea | 30.7 | 29.4 | 23.2 | 24.0 | 22.1 | 28.3 | 23.6 |

Explain why the scientist should not use the Wilcoxon test to analyse his results.

Q3 A scientist was investigating whether or not Cognitive Behavioural Therapy (CBT) is an effective treatment for depression. She used a questionnaire to calculate a score on a depression index for 5 participants who had been diagnosed with depression. Each participant was then given two months of regular CBT sessions, at the end of which the scientist asked them to complete the questionnaire again. Here are her results:

| | Participant | | | | |
|---|---|---|---|---|---|
| Depression index score | 1 | 2 | 3 | 4 | 5 |
| Before CBT | 41 | 38 | 45 | 42 | 41 |
| After CBT | 39 | 32 | 33 | 36 | 32 |

Would it be more appropriate to use a one-tailed or a two-tailed test in this study? Explain your answer.

Q4 A psychologist wanted to know if regular exercise decreased anxiety levels. She recruited 6 volunteers and measured their anxiety levels using a questionnaire. The volunteers then completed a 6 week exercise program, after which she measured their anxiety levels again. Her results are shown in the table below.

| | Participant | | | | | |
|---|---|---|---|---|---|---|
| Anxiety test score | 1 | 2 | 3 | 4 | 5 | 6 |
| Before exercise program | 35 | 41 | 22 | 27 | 33 | 34 |
| After exercise program | 28 | 39 | 23 | 26 | 30 | 35 |

a) Is the alternative hypothesis directional or non-directional?

b) What is the null hypothesis of this investigation?

c) Given that $T = 4$, are these results significant at the 0.05 level?

d) What conclusion can the psychologist draw from her results?

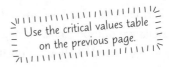
Use the critical values table on the previous page.

Q5 A psychologist was investigating whether the amount people eat is affected by how much sleep they had the night before. He measured how many calories seven participants consumed from an open buffet on the day following a good night's sleep and compared it to the number of calories they consumed from the same buffet after a night of disturbed sleep. His results are shown in the table below.

| | Participant | | | | | | |
|---|---|---|---|---|---|---|---|
| Food consumed (kcal) | 1 | 2 | 3 | 4 | 5 | 6 | 7 |
| After a good night's sleep | 547 | 615 | 782 | 704 | 656 | 531 | 730 |
| After disturbed sleep | 489 | 750 | 751 | 819 | 634 | 612 | 647 |

a) Given $T = 11$, are the psychologist's results significant at the 0.05 level?

b) Draw a conclusion from the psychologists results.

## *Wilcoxon counted two by two, hoorah, hoorah...*

*The main thing to be careful of here is using this test in the right places — you need two results per person. And remember, T needs to be equal to or less than the critical value for a result to be significant. Once you've mastered those two vital pieces of information, you'll be singing all the way to exam results day. Weeeeeeeeeeeeeeeee....*

# Spearman's Rho

*Spearman's rho* and *scattergrams* go together like statistics and frustration... *It's a good idea to have a look back at pages 28-29 before you start, as otherwise this could all be about to get a bit baffling.*

## Spearman's Rho is All About Correlations

A researcher is investigating whether the number of cigarettes smokers smoke per day is **correlated** with how neurotic they are. He might get results that look like...

...this...
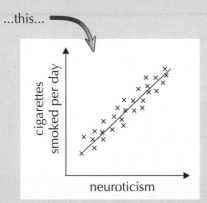

This looks like a strong correlation. All the points are near the line.

...or this...
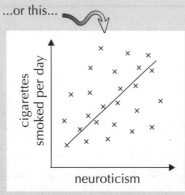

This looks like a weak correlation. The points are quite spread out.

...or this...
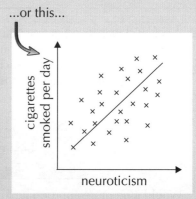

This is somewhere in between. Some of the points are a long way off the line, but a lot are very close too.

The researcher can calculate Spearman's rho to get a **single numerical value** (or **correlation coefficient**) for his results.

This makes it easy to see how weak or strong a correlation is without relying on the **line of best fit**.

You can use the value of Spearman's rho to see if your correlation is statistically **significant**.

## Spearman's Rho Tells You How Strong a Correlation is, and if it's Significant

The size and sign of Spearman's rho tells you about the strength and direction of a correlation.

1) Spearman's rho can take any value from –1 to 1, depending on your results.

2) A negative number shows a **negative correlation** (see page 29).

3) A positive number shows a **positive correlation**.

4) The **further away from zero** Spearman's rho is, the **stronger the correlation**. For example...

... $r_s = 0.08$ shows a very weak positive correlation.

... $r_s = -0.79$ shows a strong negative correlation.

... $r_s = 0.37$ shows a moderate positive correlation.

*Zero means there is no correlation at all.*

## A Formula is Used to Calculate Spearman's Rho

Here's the formula for calculating Spearman's rho.
(But don't panic — you **won't** be asked to write it down from memory in the exam. Phew.)

This stands for Spearman's rho.

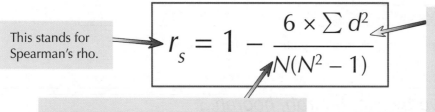

$$r_s = 1 - \frac{6 \times \sum d^2}{N(N^2 - 1)}$$

*d* is a bit tricky. It's the difference between a participant's rankings for the two **variables** you're investigating (but don't worry too much about this).

*N* is the number of observations you have — for example the number of participants.

# Spearman's Rho

## Use the *Critical Values Table* to See if the *Correlation* is *Significant*

After calculating Spearman's rho, you can find out if your correlation is significant...

1) Check whether your **alternative hypothesis** was **directional** or **non-directional** (see page 36).

2) If your alternative hypothesis was:

- **non-directional** then you need to look up the **critical value** of Spearman's rho for your **significance level** and number of observations in a **two-tailed** test table.

- **directional** then you need to look up the critical value of Spearman's rho for your significance level and number of observations in a **one-tailed** test table.

*You don't need to know about why you need to use two-tailed or one-tailed tests depending on whether or not the alternative hypothesis is directional — just remember directional is one-tailed and non-directional is two-tailed.*

3) If your value of Spearman's rho is **equal to or greater than** the critical value, then you have a significant result and can **reject the null hypothesis**.

Calculating Spearman's rho involves ranking variables in **size order**. This means you can **only** use it when **both variables** can be put in **size order**, and you're interested in whether there is a **correlation** between them.

*This test works for ordinal data (see page 64).*

### Worked Example

A researcher is investigating whether people who work more hours per week have higher stress levels. He starts to conduct a Spearman's rho on the data and calculates $\sum d^2 = 24.5$.

**Describe the correlation between stress-level and hours worked.**
**Is the correlation significant at the 0.05 level?**

| Participant | Stress rating (on a scale of 1-20) | Average number of hours worked per week |
|:---:|:---:|:---:|
| 1 | 5 | 14 |
| 2 | 12 | 20 |
| 3 | 14 | 42 |
| 4 | 7 | 7.5 |
| 5 | 18 | 49 |
| 6 | 6 | 25 |
| 7 | 10 | 23 |
| 8 | 14 | 37.5 |
| 9 | 16 | 38.5 |
| 10 | 13 | 38 |

**1** **Work out N.**

$N = 10$ ← *This is just the number of participants in the study.*

**2** **Put your value of $\sum d^2$ into the formula to find Spearman's rho, $r_s$.**

The formula for $r_s$ is :

$$r_s = 1 - \frac{6 \times \sum d^2}{N(N^2 - 1)}$$

So... $r_s = 1 - \frac{6 \times 24.5}{10(10^2 - 1)} = 1 - \frac{147}{990} = 0.85151... = \mathbf{0.852 \text{ to 3 s.f.}}$

*Use 3 s.f. (or 3 d.p) here.*

*There were 10 participants, so $N = 10$.*

**3** **Describe the correlation to answer the first part of the question.**

1) 0.852 is positive, so there is a **positive correlation** between stress levels and the average number of hours worked in a week.

2) 0.852 is pretty close to 1, so the correlation is **strong**.

> There is a strong positive correlation between stress level and the average number of hours worked per week.

*I was going to make a joke about Spearman's row but I ran out of space. Shame, it was a really funny one, too...*

# Spearman's Rho

**4** *Use a critical values table to find out if your correlation is significant.*

1) You need to know the number of participants (*N*). This was 10.

2) You need to know whether the hypothesis was **directional** or **non-directional** so you can choose between the **one-tailed test** and the **two-tailed test**.

3) You need to know the **significance level**.

4) Look up your number of participants and level of significance on a critical values table for Spearman's rho:

> The hypothesis was directional so use a one-tailed test.

### Worked Example

A researcher is investigating **whether people who work more hours per week have higher stress levels**. He starts to conduct a Spearman's rho on the data and calculates $\sum d^2 = 24.5$.

**Describe the correlation between stress-level and hours worked.**
**Is the correlation significant at the 0.05 level?**

The significance level is 0.05.

Find the column for a one-tailed test where $p \leq 0.05$...

... and the row for *N* = 10.

So, the critical value of $r_s$ = **0.564**

| | Level of significance for two-tailed test | | | |
|---|---|---|---|---|
| | *0.10* | *0.05* | *0.02* | *0.01* |
| | Level of significance for one-tailed test | | | |
| *N* | *0.05* | *0.025* | *0.01* | *0.005* |
| 8 | 0.643 | 0.738 | 0.833 | 0.881 |
| 9 | 0.600 | 0.700 | 0.783 | 0.833 |
| 10 | 0.564 | 0.648 | 0.745 | 0.794 |
| 11 | 0.536 | 0.618 | 0.709 | 0.755 |
| 12 | 0.503 | 0.587 | 0.671 | 0.727 |

> 0.876 is **greater than** 0.564 so **the correlation is significant at the 0.05 level**.

---

## Practice Questions

**Q1** For each of these values of $r_s$, say how strong the correlation is, and whether it is positive or negative.

a) $r_s = 0.95$     b) $r_s = -0.95$     c) $r_s = -0.5$     d) $r_s = 0.1$     e) $r_s = 0.000$

**Q2** A psychologist conducts research to find out if there is a significant correlation at the 0.05 level between two variables. He has results from 8 participants.
Use the table above to find the critical value of $r_s$ he needs to use if:
a) his alternative hypothesis is directional,
b) his alternative hypothesis is non-directional.

**Q3** A psychologist hypothesised that the more superstitious someone is, the higher their anxiety level will be.
He used a questionnaire to collect data on how superstitious 20 people were (on a scale of 1-10) and correlated these results with their score on an anxiety test.
His results had an $r_s$ value of 0.278.
a) Use the table on the right to find out whether his results were significant at the 5% level.
b) What should his conclusion be?

| | Level of significance for two-tailed test | | | |
|---|---|---|---|---|
| | *0.10* | *0.05* | *0.02* | *0.01* |
| | Level of significance for one-tailed test | | | |
| *N* | *0.05* | *0.025* | *0.01* | *0.005* |
| 16 | 0.429 | 0.503 | 0.582 | 0.635 |
| 17 | 0.414 | 0.485 | 0.566 | 0.615 |
| 18 | 0.401 | 0.472 | 0.550 | 0.600 |
| 19 | 0.391 | 0.460 | 0.535 | 0.584 |
| 20 | 0.380 | 0.447 | 0.520 | 0.570 |
| 21 | 0.370 | 0.435 | 0.508 | 0.556 |
| 22 | 0.361 | 0.425 | 0.496 | 0.544 |

---

## That Spearman has a lot to answer for...

*The formula for Spearman's rho is full of odd looking symbols and letters, but you <u>don't</u> have to learn it for the exam. Instead, after you've calmed down, get some practice at finding the right critical value from the critical values table.*

# Pearson's *r*

*If Spearman had a tough older brother, he'd be called Pearson. That's because **Pearson's r** gives you a correlation coefficient as well — but it's a much tougher test with a really nasty formula (what a meanie). Take a look at it here...*

## Pearson's *r* Gives You a **Correlation Coefficient**

Eight participants, ranging in age, were asked to complete a puzzle task.
The time each participant took to complete the task was recorded.

| Participant | 1 | 2 | 3 | 4 | 5 | 6 | 7 | 8 |
|---|---|---|---|---|---|---|---|---|
| Age | 12 | 16 | 20 | 24 | 28 | 32 | 36 | 40 |
| Completion Time (seconds) | 14 | 18 | 22 | 26 | 30 | 34 | 38 | 42 |

Here, the older the participant, the longer they take to complete the task. This indicates a positive correlation.

Take a look back at page 29 to see what the graphs will look like for each type of correlation.

| Participant | 1 | 2 | 3 | 4 | 5 | 6 | 7 | 8 |
|---|---|---|---|---|---|---|---|---|
| Age | 40 | 18 | 20 | 30 | 36 | 50 | 30 | 40 |
| Completion Time (seconds) | 32 | 36 | 10 | 24 | 18 | 12 | 46 | 20 |

There doesn't seem to be any correlation between these. Some of the younger participants take a longer time to complete the task...

... and some of the older participants take a shorter time to complete the task

**Pearson's *r*** investigates the **association** between two variables.
The **correlation coefficient** is called *r*, and as with Spearman's rho, this is a value between **–1** and **+1**.

## Pearson's *r* Tells You How **Strong** the Correlation Is

The size and sign of Pearson's *r* tells you about the strength and direction of a correlation — just like Spearman's rho.

1) A **positive** number shows a **positive correlation**. Both variables rise or fall in the **same direction** — i.e. they'll both go up together, or both go down together.

2) A **negative** number shows a **negative correlation** (see p.29). One variable **goes up** as the other **goes down**.

3) The **closer** Pearson's *r* is to –1 or +1, the **stronger the correlation**. For example...

> ... *r* = 0.98 shows a very strong positive correlation.
> ... *r* = –0.15 shows a weak negative correlation.
> ... *r* = –0.41 shows a moderate negative correlation.

Zero means there is no correlation at all.

## You'll Need to Calculate the **Degrees of Freedom** for **Pearson's *r***

Before you can use the critical values table for Pearson's *r*, you need to know the degrees of freedom. It's easy if you know the number of participants, *N*.

> degrees of freedom (*df*) = *N* – 2

Psst... here's the formula for Pearson's *r*. (And here's my reaction to it — ARGH!)

$$r = \frac{N(\Sigma xy) - (\Sigma x)(\Sigma y)}{\sqrt{[N\Sigma x^2 - (\Sigma x)^2] \ [N\Sigma y^2 - (\Sigma y)^2]}}$$

But don't worry — you don't have to learn it. I just didn't want it to feel left out...

• Once you've calculated *df*, decide whether your hypothesis is **one-tailed** or **two-tailed**.

• Then using this and the appropriate **significance level**, find your **critical value** using the correct critical values table.

• If the value for *r* is **greater than or equal to** the critical value, the association between the variables is **significant**.

# Pearson's *r*

A psychologist hypothesises that people who take longer to run 2 km have slower reaction times. She records the time 10 participants take to run 2 km. Each participant then completes a reaction time experiment, and their scores are noted.
She conducts a Pearson's *r* test on the data, calculating $r = -0.152$ (3 s.f.).

**Describe the correlation between running time and reaction time.**
**Is this correlation significant at the 0.05 level?**

**①** *Describe the correlation to answer the first part of the question.*

1) –0.152 is negative, so there is a **negative correlation** between running time and reaction time.

2) –0.152 is fairly far away from –1, so the correlation is **weak**.

> A negative correlation means that running time increases as reaction time decreases, or that running time decreases as reaction time increases.

> There is a weak negative correlation between running time and reaction time.

**②** *Use the number of participants in this study to work out the degrees of freedom.*

$$df = N - 2 = 10 - 2 = 8$$

Remember — *N* is the number of participants in the study.

Rimi was ecstatic — finding the value of *df* wasn't as difficult as she'd first thought.

**③** *Use a critical values table to find out if your correlation is significant.*

1) Decide whether the hypothesis is directional or non-directional. Here, it's directional — she says that people who **take longer** have a **slower** reaction time, so she'll use a **one-tailed test**.

2) Make sure you choose the right **significance level**. This question asks whether the results are significant at the **0.05 level**.

3) Now use your value of *df* to read off the **critical value**.

4) When comparing your value of *r* to the critical value, you can ignore the negative sign. Remember, *r* needs to be greater than or equal to the critical value to be significant.

> The critical value of *r* = **0.549**

*N* = 8, so read along this row.

> 0.152 is **less than** 0.549, so the correlation is **not significant** at the 0.05 level.

| | Level of significance for two-tailed test | | | |
|---|---|---|---|---|
| | **0.10** | **0.05** | **0.02** | **0.01** |
| | Level of significance for one-tailed test | | | |
| *df* | **0.05** | **0.025** | **0.01** | **0.005** |
| 2 | 0.900 | 0.950 | 0.980 | 0.990 |
| 3 | 0.805 | 0.878 | 0.934 | 0.959 |
| 4 | 0.729 | 0.811 | 0.882 | 0.917 |
| 5 | 0.669 | 0.754 | 0.833 | 0.874 |
| 6 | 0.622 | 0.707 | 0.789 | 0.834 |
| 7 | 0.582 | 0.666 | 0.750 | 0.798 |
| 8 | 0.549 | 0.632 | 0.716 | 0.765 |
| 9 | 0.521 | 0.602 | 0.685 | 0.735 |
| 10 | 0.497 | 0.576 | 0.658 | 0.708 |

## Practice Questions

Q1 Describe the correlations indicated by each of these values of *r*.

a) $r = -0.99$

b) $r = 0.03$

c) $r = 0.48$

d) $r = -0.17$

e) $r = 0.00$

f) $r = 0.875$

# Pearson's *r*

**Q2** A researcher is assessing the association between people's heights and stress levels.
He conducts a Pearson's *r* test on his data, and calculates *r* = 0.083.

Describe the correlation he finds between people's heights and stress levels.

**Q3** A psychologist hypothesised that there would be a relationship between the time people took to complete a difficult puzzle and their IQ. She recorded how long they took to complete the puzzle task, after taking an IQ test. Her results are shown in the table below.

| Participant | 1 | 2 | 3 | 4 | 5 | 6 | 7 | 8 | 9 | 10 | 11 | 12 |
|---|---|---|---|---|---|---|---|---|---|---|---|---|
| Time taken to complete puzzle task (seconds) | 96 | 123 | 54 | 87 | 94 | 62 | 88 | 70 | 115 | 121 | 104 | 155 |
| IQ | 80 | 100 | 90 | 82 | 60 | 50 | 48 | 76 | 100 | 111 | 108 | 99 |

a) Is this hypothesis directional or non-directional?

b) Write down the null hypothesis for this research.

c) What is the value of *df* for this research?

**Q4** A psychologist who was looking at different learning styles wanted to test the hypothesis that people who are good at Maths are also good at Science. He asked seven participants to complete a Maths test, followed by a Science test. Their results are shown in the table. He then conducted a Pearson's *r* test on the data, and got a value of *r* = 0.759 (3 s.f.).

a) Describe the correlation shown by this data.

b) Is this hypothesis directional or non-directional?

c) What is the value of *df* for this research?

d) Use the critical values table on the previous page to determine if his results are significant at the 0.01 level.

| Participant | Maths test score (%) | Science test score (%) |
|---|---|---|
| 1 | 23 | 35 |
| 2 | 16 | 20 |
| 3 | 80 | 65 |
| 4 | 95 | 99 |
| 5 | 46 | 90 |
| 6 | 46 | 82 |
| 7 | 64 | 76 |

**Q5** A researcher hypothesises that there is a relationship between intelligence and number of criminal offences among criminals. She records the IQ of each participant alongside how many criminal offences they have been charged for during the past five years. She then analyses the data set below using a Pearson's *r* test, calculating *r* = 0.910.

| Participant | 1 | 2 | 3 | 4 | 5 | 6 | 7 | 8 | 9 |
|---|---|---|---|---|---|---|---|---|---|
| IQ | 45 | 65 | 78 | 90 | 52 | 100 | 152 | 80 | 60 |
| Number of criminal offences | 3 | 1 | 2 | 14 | 4 | 18 | 32 | 17 | 6 |

a) Is this hypothesis directional or non-directional?

b) Write down the null hypothesis for this research.

c) What is the value of *df* for this research?

d) Use the critical values table on the previous page to determine if her results are significant at the 0.05 level.

---

## *Pearson's Arrrrrr — the pirate version of Pearson's r...*

*Pearson's r is very similar to Spearman's rho. The key difference is that Spearman's rho uses ordinal data, whereas Pearson's r uses interval data. If you need a handy way of remembering that difference — Spearman's rho ends in 'o' and ordinal starts with 'o'. Arrrrrr, me hearties... shiver me timbers... heave ho... (I'll stop now).*

# Related *t*-Test

*The **related t-test** looks at whether there's a significance difference between two sets of related data — go figure...*
*So here are a few lovely pages to explain all this, followed by some practice questions to finish it all off.  Hoorah.*

## The **Related t-Test** is Used For **Repeated Measures** Designs

*It's also called a dependent t-test.*

An experiment was conducted to investigate the effect of caffeine on the time taken to complete a jigsaw puzzle.
Five participants were asked to complete a jigsaw puzzle.  Their time taken to complete the jigsaw was recorded.
After drinking 500 ml of coffee, they were then asked to complete another jigsaw, of similar difficulty.
Their time taken to complete this second jigsaw was also recorded.

BEFORE:
**20 minutes**
AFTER:
**16 minutes**

BEFORE:
**30 minutes**
AFTER:
**21 minutes**

BEFORE:
**26 minutes**
AFTER:
**18 minutes**

This person took less time to complete a jigsaw after drinking coffee.

BEFORE:
**22 minutes**
AFTER:
**28 minutes**

This person took longer to complete a jigsaw after drinking coffee.

BEFORE:
**24 minutes**
AFTER:
**24 minutes**

Caffeine appeared to have no effect on this person — they took the same amount of time to complete a jigsaw before and after drinking coffee.

It's hard to tell if caffeine does have an effect on memory performance.
But a **related *t*-test** can see if any difference is due to chance or not.

## The **Related t-Test** Uses **Interval** Data

To use a related *t*-test, your data must be...

- From a **repeated measures**, or **matched pairs** design.
- **Interval** data.
- Normally distributed (see page 32).

*Remember, in a repeated measures designs, the same participants take part in both conditions. In a matched pairs design, different participants are used for each condition, but they're matched on variables such as age, gender, IQ, etc.*

## Use **N – 1** to Calculate the **Degrees of Freedom**

You'll need to calculate the degrees of freedom (*df*) for a related *t*-test.

1) Start by counting up the number of participants.  This is *N*.

2) Then take away 1.  Simple.

degrees of freedom (*df*) = *N* – 1

3) A nasty-looking formula is used to find the observed value, *t*.
(Don't worry — you **don't** need to know it for your exam.)

*If you're interested in the nasty-looking formula for a related t-test, here it is.*

$$t = \frac{\Sigma d}{\sqrt{\dfrac{N\Sigma d^2 - (\Sigma d)^2}{N-1}}}$$

*But just wait until you see the formula on page 55.  You're in for a real treat...*

# Related *t*-Test

## Look Up the **Critical Value** in a **Critical Values** Table

- Once you know *t*, and you know the degrees of freedom, you can look up the **critical value** in a critical values table to see if your results are **significant**.

- The observed value, *t*, must be **greater than or equal to** the critical value to be significant.

### Worked Example

Eight participants took part in an experiment comparing people's stress levels when holding a toy snake with their stress levels when holding a real snake. The psychologist hypothesised that participants holding a real snake would have higher stress levels than those holding a toy snake.

Stress levels were measured by recording the blood cortisol level (a stress hormone) before and after holding the snake. She conducted a related *t*-test on the data, and found an observed value of $t = 3.865$.

**Did participants have significantly higher stress levels when holding a real snake compared to when holding a toy snake? Use a significance level of 0.01.**

**1** *Use the number of participants in the study to work out the degrees of freedom.*

1) There are eight participants in the study.
2) $df = N - 1$, so $df = 8 - 1 = 7$.

$N = 7$

**2** *Decide if the hypothesis was directional or non-directional.*

The hypothesis was **directional**, so use the **one-tailed test**.

Stuff the critical values table — Bart and Enid's picnic table was far more practical.

**3** *Use a critical values table to find out if your result is significant.*

The **significance level** you're interested in is 0.01.

| | Level of significance for two-tailed test | | | |
|---|---|---|---|---|
| | **0.10** | **0.05** | **0.02** | **0.01** |
| | Level of significance for one-tailed test | | | |
| **df** | **0.05** | **0.025** | **0.01** | **0.005** |
| 1 | 6.314 | 12.706 | 31.821 | 63.657 |
| 2 | 2.920 | 4.303 | 6.965 | 9.925 |
| 3 | 2.353 | 3.182 | 4.541 | 5.841 |
| 4 | 2.132 | 2.776 | 3.747 | 4.604 |
| 5 | 2.015 | 2.571 | 3.365 | 4.032 |
| 6 | 1.943 | 2.447 | 3.143 | 3.707 |
| 7 | 1.895 | 2.365 | 2.998 | 3.499 |
| 8 | 1.860 | 2.306 | 2.896 | 3.355 |
| 9 | 1.833 | 2.262 | 2.821 | 3.250 |

Abridged from Statistical Tables for Biological Agricultural and Medical Research (6th ed.) © 1963 R.A Fisher and F. Yates. Reprinted with permission of Pearson Education Limited.

This is the column for a one-tailed test with a *p* of 0.01.

This is the row for $N = 7$

The critical value of *t* is **2.998**.

3.865 is **greater than** 2.998 so the results **are significant**.

**People had significantly higher stress levels after holding a real snake than after holding a toy snake.**

# Related *t*-Test

**Q1** What type of data must a study have collected in order for a related *t*-test to be an appropriate statistical test?

**Q2** A psychologist conducts an experiment to assess if exercise affects participants' scores on a spelling test. She asks 50 participants to take part. Each participant completes one spelling test before an exercise drill, and one spelling test after an exercise drill. She records the percentage of words they spelt correctly in each test.
   a) Write down an alternative hypothesis for this study.
   b) Write down the null hypothesis for this study.
   c) Calculate the degrees of freedom for this study.

**Q3** A researcher hypotheses that there is a relationship between sleep deprivation and calorie consumption. 22 participants take part in her experiment. All participants record how much they eat in one day, following a night of 8 hours sleep. A week later, they are then asked to record how much they eat in one day, following a night of only 4 hours sleep.
   a) Is her hypothesis directional or non-directional?
   b) Write a null hypothesis for this research.
   c) Calculate the degrees of freedom for this study.
   d) Find the critical value for this study at the 0.01 level using the critical values table on the right.

| Level of significance for two-tailed test | | | |
|---|---|---|---|
| 0.10 | 0.05 | 0.02 | 0.01 |
| Level of significance for one-tailed test | | | |
| *df* | 0.05 | 0.025 | 0.01 | 0.005 |
| 16 | 1.746 | 2.120 | 2.583 | 2.921 |
| 17 | 1.740 | 2.110 | 2.567 | 2.898 |
| 18 | 1.734 | 2.101 | 2.552 | 2.878 |
| 19 | 1.729 | 2.093 | 2.539 | 2.861 |
| 20 | 1.725 | 2.086 | 2.528 | 2.845 |
| 21 | 1.721 | 2.080 | 2.518 | 2.831 |
| 22 | 1.717 | 2.074 | 2.508 | 2.819 |

Abridged from Statistical Tables for Biological Agricultural and Medical Research (6th ed.) © 1963 R.A Fisher and F. Yates. Reprinted with permission of Pearson Education Limited.

**Q4** A psychologist hypothesised that people would donate significantly more money to charity after reading a sad story in a newspaper than they would after reading a happy story in a newspaper. Twenty participants took part in the study. All participants were asked to read a sad story on one day and then a happy story the next day. They were given £5 after reading each story. Each time, when they had finished reading the article, they were asked whether they would like to donate any money to charity. The amount they donated was recorded. The psychologist collected the data and conducted a related *t*-test on the data. He calculated an observed value of *t* = 3.851 (3 d.p.).
   a) Use the table above to find out whether his results were significant at the 5% level.
   b) What should his conclusion be?

**Q5** A researcher investigated the reaction times of people before and after they'd carried out a monotonous task. He hypothesised that participants' reaction times would be longer after they had completed the monotonous task than their reaction times before the task. The results of the study are shown below.

| Participant | 1 | 2 | 3 | 4 | 5 | 6 |
|---|---|---|---|---|---|---|
| Reaction time before monotonous task (seconds) | 5.4 | 2.6 | 3.1 | 2.5 | 6.2 | 1.2 |
| Reaction time after monotonous task (seconds) | 6.8 | 3.5 | 4.8 | 3.1 | 6.2 | 1.8 |

He conducted a related *t*-test, calculating an observed value of *t* = 3.468 (3 d.p.).

Use the critical values table on the previous page to determine whether these results are significant at $p \leq 0.01$.

---

## Assam, Darjeeling, Earl Grey, Lapsang Souchong — *t*-tests are my thing...

*Bother. Wrong sort of tea. But these pages are still important. Make sure you remember when to use a related t-test (with interval data, in repeated measures designs), and how to calculate the degrees of freedom (N – 1).*

# Unrelated *t*-Test

*It's a bit like not having a biscuit with your cup of tea — it seems wrong to have a related t-test without an **unrelated t-test**. So here it is. But don't get freaked out when you see the formula. You won't be asked to remember it in the exam.*

## The **Unrelated t-Test** is Used For **Independent Measures** Designs

A psychologist wants to investigate how horror and comedy films can affect stress levels. She uses two different groups of participants to test her hypothesis. One group watches a horror film and the other watches a comedy film. Their stress levels are measured straight after watching, and each participant is given a stress score.

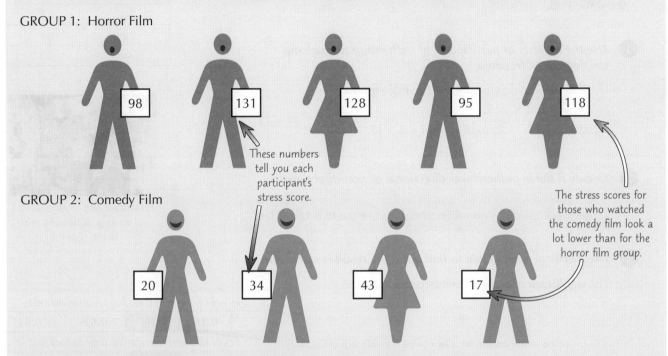

GROUP 1: Horror Film

98    131    128    95    118

These numbers tell you each participant's stress score.

GROUP 2: Comedy Film

20    34    43    17

The stress scores for those who watched the comedy film look a lot lower than for the horror film group.

An unrelated *t*-test is used on data from **two separate groups**. It tells you whether the difference between the two groups is significant, or just down to chance.

## The **Unrelated t-Test** Uses **Interval** Data

To use an unrelated *t*-test, your data must be...

- From different participants (so it's an **independent measures** design). The groups don't even have to be the same size.
- **Interval** data.
- Normally distributed (see page 32).

It's also called an independent *t*-test.

## Calculate the **Degrees of Freedom** To Help Find the **Critical Value**

Before you can use the critical values table for this test, you need to work out the degrees of freedom.

1) Count up the **number** of participants in each group. Call the first group *X* and the second group *Y*.

2) Then call the number of participants in the **first group** $N_X$ and the number of participants in the **second group** $N_Y$.

3) Plug the numbers into the formula: $df = N_X + N_Y - 2$.

4) Once you know *df* and the **significance level**, you can look up the **critical value** in the critical values table.

Here it is... the nastiest looking equation in this section. Lovely isn't it?

$$t = \frac{M_x - M_y}{\sqrt{\left[\frac{\left(\Sigma x^2 - \frac{(\Sigma x)^2}{N_x}\right) + \left(\Sigma y^2 - \frac{(\Sigma y)^2}{N_y}\right)}{N_x + N_y - 2}\right]\left[\frac{1}{N_x} + \frac{1}{N_y}\right]}}$$

The observed value, *t*, must be **greater than or equal to** the critical value for the results to be significant.

# Unrelated *t*-Test

A psychologist hypothesises that there will be a significant difference in the time males and females take to complete a logic puzzle. Participants are asked to complete a logic puzzle and their times are recorded, in seconds. The results are shown in the table on the right. He uses an unrelated *t*-test to calculate an observed value of $t = -0.286$ (3 d.p.).

**Use the critical values table below to decide if his results are significant at the 0.05 level.**

| Female score (s) | Male score (s) |
|---|---|
| 58 | 24 |
| 67 | 45 |
| 64 | 75 |
| 29 | 35 |
| 70 | 82 |
| 12 | 65 |
| — | 49 |

**1** *Use the number of participants in each group to work out the degrees of freedom.*

1) Call the female group $X$ and the male group $Y$.
2) $N_X = 6$ and $N_Y = 7$.
3) $df = N_X + N_Y - 2$, so $df = 6 + 7 - 2 = 11$.

$N = 11$

An independent *t*-test is almost as exciting as heading into space. Almost.

**2** *Decide if the hypothesis was directional or non-directional.*

The hypothesis was **non-directional**, so use the **two-tailed test**.

**3** *Use a critical values table to find out if the result is significant.*

The **significance level** you're interested in is 0.05.

This is the column for a two-tailed test with a *p* of 0.05.

The critical value of *t* is **2.201**.

0.286 is **less than** 2.201 so the results are **not significant**.

Ignore the minus sign in the observed value when you're comparing it with the value from the critical values table.

|  | Level of significance for two-tailed test | | | |
|---|---|---|---|---|
|  | **0.10** | **0.05** | **0.02** | **0.01** |
|  | Level of significance for one-tailed test | | | |
| **df** | **0.05** | **0.025** | **0.01** | **0.005** |
| 4 | 2.132 | 2.776 | 3.747 | 4.604 |
| 5 | 2.015 | 2.571 | 3.365 | 4.032 |
| 6 | 1.943 | 2.447 | 3.143 | 3.707 |
| 7 | 1.895 | 2.365 | 2.998 | 3.499 |
| 8 | 1.860 | 2.306 | 2.896 | 3.355 |
| 9 | 1.833 | 2.262 | 2.821 | 3.250 |
| 10 | 1.812 | 2.228 | 2.764 | 3.169 |
| 11 | 1.796 | 2.201 | 2.718 | 3.106 |
| 12 | 1.782 | 2.179 | 2.681 | 3.055 |

This is the row for *N* = 11.

**There is no significant difference in the time taken to complete a logic puzzle between males and females.**

Abridged from Statistical Tables for Biological Agricultural and Medical Research (6th ed.) © 1963 R.A Fisher and F. Yates. Reprinted with permission of Pearson Education Limited.

## Practice Questions

Q1 Use the critical values table above to determine whether these observed values are significant.

a) $t = 3.645$ for a two-tailed test at significance level 0.01 when $df = 6$.

b) $t = 1.965$ for a one-tailed test, where $p \leq 0.05$ when $df = 10$.

c) $t = 2.851$ for a two-tailed test, where $p \leq 0.01$ when $df = 7$.

d) $t = 1.782$ for a one-tailed test at the 5% level when $df = 12$.

# Unrelated *t*-Test

**Q2** A psychologist wants to investigate the impact of listening to music on scores in an IQ test. A group of ten participants are asked to complete an IQ test in silence. They are then asked to complete a similar IQ test, but whilst listening to music. Their scores are recorded and compared using an unrelated *t*-test.

Explain why this is the incorrect statistical test to use.

**Q3** A psychologist wants to compare memory ability between students in Year 12 and students in Year 13.
  a) Write down an alternative hypothesis for this study.
  b) Write down the null hypothesis for this study.

**Q4** A researcher hypothesises that there will be a significant difference between resting heart rate depending on whether a person lives in a village or a city. Two groups of participants took part in the study. One group had lived in a village for 10 years, whereas the second group had lived in a city for 10 years. All participants had their resting heart rate taken each day for a month to provide an average resting heart rate.

| | Average resting heart rate (beats per minute) | | | | | | | | |
|---|---|---|---|---|---|---|---|---|---|
| Village | 58 | 72 | 80 | 60 | 64 | 61 | 59 | — | — |
| City | 84 | 102 | 115 | 100 | 97 | 98 | 60 | 55 | 71 |

  a) Is the hypothesis in this study directional or non-directional?
  b) Write down the null hypothesis for this study.
  c) Calculate the degrees of freedom for this study.

**Q5** A psychologist wants to investigate the effectiveness of a new computer programme for spelling improvement. Two groups of children took part in the experiment — one group used the programme for a week and one group didn't. At the end of the week, both groups were asked to spell a list of 30 words. Their results are shown in the table below. The psychologist conducted an unrelated *t*-test on the data, calculating an observed value of *t* = 4.052 (3 d.p.).

| | Number of correctly spelt words | | | | | | |
|---|---|---|---|---|---|---|---|
| Computer programme | 28 | 27 | 26 | 30 | 22 | 30 | 29 |
| No computer programme | 24 | 23 | 24 | 20 | 18 | 22 | 16 |

  a) Is the hypothesis in this study directional or non-directional?
  b) Calculate the degrees of freedom for this study.
  c) Use the critical values table on the previous page to find the critical value for this experiment at a significance level of 0.01.
  d) Write a conclusion for this experiment.

**Q6** A psychologist is investigating the effectiveness of a new drug treatment at reducing blood pressure.
  a) Write down a possible one-tailed hypothesis for this study.
  b) The psychologist would like to use an unrelated *t*-test to analyse the data. Design a study which would enable her to do this.

---

## *Sausages, bacon, tomato, eggs — my brain's as fried as my breakfast...*

*Unrelated t-tests are similar to related t-tests (which makes sense when you think about it). It's sort of obvious from the name that groups of participants aren't related in an unrelated t-test. But you can have groups of different sizes. Make sure you're familiar with all this stuff, and that you've had a good bash at the practice questions.*

# Mann-Whitney Test

*The **Mann-Whitney test** allows you to find out whether the differences in a variable between two independent groups are **significant**. Take a look at these pages to discover more about this lovely little test...*

## The **Mann-Whitney Test** is About Finding **Differences** Between **Groups**

Imagine you want to compare the test scores of a group of men with the scores of a group of women...

28    32    42    30    38

In general, it looks like the women have done better than the men.

However, there is quite a lot of overlap between the two groups.

48    36    38    37    42

The **Mann-Whitney test** lets you see whether differences like this are **significant** or not.

## Make Sure that the **Mann-Whitney Test** is Right For **Your Data**

To use a Mann-Whitney test, you must have...

1) Data from **two different groups** that can be put in **order of size**. It's OK if there are more participants in one group than the other.

   *This test works for ordinal or interval data (see page 64).*

2) **One measure only** from each participant — no participant should appear in both groups. Your participants shouldn't have been able to affect each other's results either.

   *This is independent data.*

If these aren't true for your data, this is the **wrong test** to use.

## The Mann-Whitney Test Uses **Two Formulas** to Calculate the **Test Statistic**

Another **test statistic**, another formula... Once again, you don't need to learn them.

For a Mann-Whitney test, you calculate a value called $U$ (the **test statistic**) for **each group** in your data, e.g. men and women. In the formula, the different groups are called **A** and **B**.

$$U_A = N_A N_B + \frac{N_A(N_A + 1)}{2} - R_A$$

$N$ is the number of people in a group.
$N_A$ is the number in group A, e.g. the men.
$N_B$ is the number in group B, e.g. the women.

$$U_B = N_A N_B + \frac{N_B(N_B + 1)}{2} - R_B$$

To calculate a Mann-Whitney test, you'd have to rank the scores, from smallest to highest.

$R$ is the **sum of the ranks** for the scores in each group.
$R_A$ is the total for group A,
$R_B$ is the total for group B.

# Mann-Whitney Test

## A *Mann-Whitney Test* Can Tell You if Your Results are **Significant**

Once you've got a value of $U$ for each of your groups...

1) Pick whichever of your two values of U is **lower**, and look it up in a **critical values table**.

2) If your value of U is **equal to or less than** the **critical value**, your result is significant and you can **reject the null hypothesis**.

*This is different from related and unrelated t-tests and Spearman's rho, where you need your test statistic to be equal to or greater than the critical value. It's something to be careful of.*

### Worked Example

A researcher was investigating whether females get higher scores than males in a psychological test. Her results are shown in the table on the right.

She conducts a Mann-Whitney test which gives her test statistics of $U_A = 19$ for males and $U_B = 6$ for females.

**Do females get significantly higher scores than males at the 0.05 level?**

| Gender | Score | | | | |
|--------|----|----|----|----|----|
| Male | 28 | 32 | 42 | 30 | 38 |
| Female | 48 | 36 | 38 | 37 | 42 |

**1** **Pick the lowest value from $U_A$ and $U_B$. Call it U.**

$U_B$ is smaller than $U_A$. So for this test $U = 6$.

*The giant dinosaur attack had caused havoc in downtown Tokyo, but at least it got Chihiro out of practising her stats tests.*

**2** **Use a critical values table to find if your result is significant.**

There's a different critical values table for each level of significance for the Mann-Whitney test, and separate tables for one or two-tailed tests.

To pick the right table, you need to:

- Decide if you need a one or two-tailed test. Remember, if the **alternative hypothesis** is **directional** you need the **one-tailed test**. If it's **non-directional** then you should use the **two-tailed test**.

- Check what your **significance level** is.

### Worked Example

A researcher was investigating **whether females get higher scores than males** in a psychological test. Her results are shown in the table on the right. She conducts a Mann-Whitney test which gives her test statistics of $U_A = 19$ for males and $U_B = 6$ for females. **Do females get significantly higher scores than males at the 0.05 level?**

*The hypothesis was directional so use a one-tailed test.*

*The significance level is 0.05*

Then you can:

1) Look up the critical value for your values of $N_A$ and $N_B$ (these might be called $N_1$ and $N_2$ in some tables).

2) Compare the critical value to your value of $U$. If your value is equal to or smaller than the critical value you can **reject the null hypothesis**.

*There were 5 males in group A.*

*There were 5 females in group B.*

**Critical values for the one-tailed Mann-Whitney test at $p = 0.05$, or the two-tailed Mann-Whitney test at $p = 0.10$.**

| | | | $N_1$ | | | |
|---|---|---|---|---|---|---|
| | | **5** | **6** | **7** | **8** | **9** |
| | **5** | 4 | 5 | 6 | 8 | 9 |
| | **6** | 5 | 7 | 8 | 10 | 12 |
| $N_2$ | **7** | 6 | 8 | 11 | 13 | 15 |
| | **8** | 8 | 10 | 13 | 15 | 18 |
| | **9** | 9 | 12 | 15 | 18 | 21 |

The critical value of $U$ is 4, and the calculated value of $U$ was 6 so the result is **not significant**. You **cannot reject the null hypothesis**.

Abridged from Fundamentals of behavioural statistics (3rd Edn.) by R. Runyon and A. Haber © 1976 McGraw-Hill Education.

**Females did not get significantly higher scores than males in this test at the 5% level.**

# Mann-Whitney Test

## Practice Questions

Use this table and the critical values table on page 59 to help you answer the questions on this page.

**Q1** What is the critical value of $U$ for a one-tailed test using a significance level of 0.05 if:

a) There are 6 participants in Group 1 and 6 participants in Group 2?

b) There are 7 participants in Group A and 8 participants in Group B?

c) There are 9 participants in Group 1 and 8 participants in Group 2?

d) There are 8 participants in Group A and 9 participants in Group B?

**Critical values for the one-tailed Mann-Whitney test at $p = 0.025$ or the two-tailed Mann-Whitney test at $p = 0.05$.**

| | | $N_1$ | | | | |
|---|---|---|---|---|---|---|
| | | 5 | 6 | 7 | 8 | 9 |
| | 5 | 2 | 3 | 5 | 6 | 7 |
| $N_2$ | 6 | 3 | 5 | 6 | 8 | 10 |
| | 7 | 5 | 6 | 8 | 10 | 12 |
| | 8 | 6 | 8 | 10 | 13 | 15 |
| | 9 | 7 | 10 | 12 | 15 | 17 |

Abridged from Fundamentals of behavioural statistics (3rd Edn.) by R. Runyon and A. Haber © 1976 McGraw-Hill Education.

**Q2** A psychologist was investigating whether a new drug reduces the symptoms of anxiety. He recruited 12 participants who showed similar levels of anxiety. Half of these 12 participants were administered the drug and the other half were given a placebo. Half an hour after administering the drug he measured the anxiety levels of all 12 participants.

He conducted a Mann-Whitney test on his data and got a value of $U = 4$.

a) Are his results significant at the 0.05 level? Explain your answer.

b) What should his conclusion be?

**Q3** A researcher hypothesised that children will play with a toy for longer if they have seen a child of the same gender playing with the toy previously, compared to a child of the other gender. He showed 6 children a video of a child of the same gender as themselves playing with a toy, and 6 children a video of a child of the other gender to themselves playing with the same toy. He then gave each child the opportunity to play with the toy, and timed how long they played with it.

His results are shown in the table below.

| Gender of child on video | Time spent playing with toy (secs) | | | | | |
|---|---|---|---|---|---|---|
| Same as participant | 192 | 331 | 275 | 341 | 280 | 310 |
| Different from participant | 175 | 187 | 238 | 236 | 154 | 300 |

a) Is the scientist's alternative hypothesis directional or non-directional?

b) What is the null hypothesis of this investigation?

c) Given that $U_A = 5$ and $U_B = 31$ for these results, what is $U$?

d) Are the researcher's results significant at the 0.05 level?

e) What conclusion can the researcher draw from his results?

**Q4** A psychologist was interested in finding out whether people with anorexia nervosa show higher levels of general anxiety than people without anorexia nervosa. She used a questionnaire to collect the following results.

| | Anxiety Score | | | | | | | | |
|---|---|---|---|---|---|---|---|---|---|
| Suffers from anorexia nervosa | 84 | 89 | 91 | 78 | 65 | 77 | 82 | 76 | 84 |
| Does not suffer from anorexia nervosa | 52 | 41 | 67 | 79 | 56 | 83 | 64 | 59 | 34 |

$U_A = 10$ and $U_B = 71$, where group A refers to those who suffer from anorexia nervosa and group B refers to those who don't suffer from anorexia nervosa.

Do her results show that people who suffer from anorexia nervosa have significantly higher levels of anxiety than people who do not suffer from anorexia nervosa, at the 5% level?

---

## Mann, I love a Whitney test...

*The most exciting feature of the Mann-Whitney test is that you can have groups of different sizes. You don't get that in statistical testing every day, that's for sure. In fact, to celebrate, I think I'll have a cup of tea and a chocolate biscuit...*

# Chi-Squared Test

*We've finally arrived at the last statistical test for this section (I bet you've been looking forward to it).*
*The **chi-squared test** might have an odd name, but it's not that hard to get your head around...*

## The **Chi-Squared Test** Looks at **Differences** in **Frequencies** Between **Groups**

An experiment was conducted to investigate whether male and female children prefer to play with a toy car or a soft toy. Thirty boys and thirty girls were given a choice of playing with either toy.

If there was no difference between boys and girls you might expect results like this:

| Gender | Preferred Toy | | |
|--------|-----|----------|-------|
| | Car | Soft toy | Total |
| Male | 15 | 15 | 30 |
| Female | 15 | 15 | 30 |
| Total | 30 | 30 | |

All the numbers in the table are the same. An equal number of boys and girls like cars and soft toys.

If there is a very strong difference between boys and girls you might get extreme results like this:

| Gender | Preferred Toy | | |
|--------|-----|----------|-------|
| | Car | Soft toy | Total |
| Male | 30 | 0 | 30 |
| Female | 0 | 30 | 30 |
| Total | 30 | 30 | |

All the boys preferred the toy car.

All the girls preferred the soft toy.

Usually, your results will be somewhere between these two extremes:

More boys liked the toy car than the soft toy.

More girls liked the soft toy than the toy car.

| Gender | Preferred Toy | | |
|--------|-----|----------|-------|
| | Car | Soft toy | Total |
| Male | 18 | 12 | 30 |
| Female | 10 | 20 | 30 |
| Total | 28 | 32 | |

The chi-squared test helps you see whether results like this are likely to be due to chance or not.

## Make Sure You're Using the **Right Test**

You can't use a chi-squared test in every experiment, so researchers need to think carefully about whether it's the right test to use before they start their analysis. To use a chi-squared test, the data must meet these requirements...

1) The data is about **frequencies** for **different categories** (e.g. colours). It's best if the categories don't have any particular **order** (like size).

   *This is called nominal data (see page 64).*

2) Each participant only appears in your results **once**, and the participants were not able to affect each other's results.

   *This is called independent data.*

If these aren't true for your data, you should use a **different test**.

# Chi-Squared Test

## The **Chi-Squared** Has a **Formula**

Here is the formula for the chi-squared test. Don't worry though — you **won't** have to learn it for the exam.

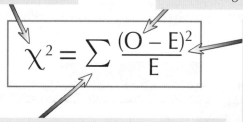

This means **chi-squared**.

'O' is the **observed frequency** for each possibility from the table (e.g. the number of boys preferring cars).

$$\chi^2 = \sum \frac{(O - E)^2}{E}$$

'E' is the **expected frequency** for each possibility from the table if the null hypothesis is true. You work out the expected frequency for each possibility like this:

$$\text{Expected frequency} = \frac{\text{row total} \times \text{column total}}{\text{overall total}}$$

Remember, this symbol means "sum of" (see page 34).

## The **Chi-Squared Test** Can Tell You if Your Results are **Significant**

Once you've got a chi-squared value...

1) Work out the **degrees of freedom (df)** for your data using this formula:

$$df = (\text{number of rows} - 1) \times (\text{number of columns} - 1)$$

Don't worry about what this means, you just need to use it to look up whether or not your result is significant.

2) Look up the **critical value** of chi-squared for your level of significance and degrees of freedom in a **critical values table**.

3) If your value for chi-squared is **greater than or equal to** the critical value, then you have a **significant** result and can **reject the null hypothesis**.

### Worked Example

A researcher investigating whether male and female children prefer to play with different sorts of toy collected the data in the table on the right.

By conducting a chi-squared test on her data, she found that $\chi^2 = 4.29$.

**Is there a significant difference in the preferred toy of male and female children? Use a significance level of 0.05.**

| Gender | Preferred Toy | | |
|--------|-----|----------|-------|
| | Car | Soft toy | Total |
| Male | 18 | 12 | 30 |
| Female | 10 | 20 | 30 |
| Total | 28 | 32 | 60 |

**1** **Work out the degrees of freedom (df).**

$$df = (2 - 1) \times (2 - 1) = \mathbf{1}$$

Remember:
$(df) = (\text{number of rows} - 1) \times (\text{number of columns} - 1)$

If the null hypothesis is true, there'll be no difference in toy preference between males and females.

**2** **Now look up the critical value of chi-squared for your significance level and degrees of freedom.**

For the result to be significant, your value of $\chi^2$ needs to be equal to or greater than the critical value.

When $df = 1$ and there's a significance level of 0.05, the critical value of chi-squared is **3.84**.

4.29 is greater than 3.84, so the results are **significantly different from chance**.

| df | Level of significance | | | | |
|----|------|------|------|-------|-------|
| | **0.20** | **0.10** | **0.05** | **0.02** | **0.01** |
| 1 | 1.64 | 2.71 | 3.84 | 5.41 | 6.64 |
| 2 | 3.22 | 4.60 | 5.99 | 7.82 | 9.21 |
| 3 | 4.64 | 6.25 | 7.82 | 9.84 | 11.34 |
| 4 | 5.99 | 7.78 | 9.49 | 11.67 | 13.28 |
| 5 | 7.29 | 9.24 | 11.07 | 13.39 | 15.09 |
| 6 | 8.56 | 10.64 | 12.59 | 15.03 | 16.81 |
| 7 | 9.80 | 12.02 | 14.07 | 16.62 | 18.48 |
| 8 | 11.03 | 13.36 | 15.51 | 18.17 | 20.09 |

**There is a significant difference in the preferred toy of male and female children.**

Abridged from Statistical Tables for Biological Agricultural and Medical Research (6th ed.) © 1963 R.A Fisher and F. Yates. Reprinted with permission of Pearson Education Limited.

# Chi-Squared Test

## Practice Questions

Q1  In a chi-squared test...

    a)  what is an observed frequency?

    b)  what is an expected frequency?

    c)  how does the chi-squared value need to compare to the critical value for your results to be significant?

Q2  Using the table on page 62, find the critical value of chi-squared...

    a)  for a significance level of 0.05 and 2 degrees of freedom.

    b)  when $p \leq 0.01$ and $df = 3$.

    c)  for a test being conducted at the 5% significance level with 6 degrees of freedom.

    d)  when $p \leq 0.1$ and $df = 1$.

Q3  A researcher is investigating if there is a relationship between whether or not parents are overweight and whether or not their children are.  She collects data via a questionnaire and performs a chi-squared test on her results.  She gets a chi-squared value of 3.85.  $df = 1$.

Use the table on page 62 to determine if her results are significantly different from chance at the 0.05 level.  What conclusion could she make?

Q4  A researcher is investigating if there is a relationship between whether or not someone watches TV in the evening and whether or not they sleep well that night.  He collects data from seven people over five days, to give him 35 observations, shown in the table on the right.  The researcher wants to use a chi-squared test to analyse this data.

Is this the correct test to use?  Explain your answer.

| TV watching | Quality of sleep | | |
| --- | --- | --- | --- |
| | Good | Poor | Total |
| Watched TV | 14 | 6 | 20 |
| Didn't watch TV | 9 | 6 | 15 |
| Total | 23 | 12 | 35 |

Q5  A psychologist wanted to know whether or not there is a difference in the rate of depression between people with an identical twin who suffers from depression and people with a non-identical twin who suffers from depression.  He collected the following data.

| | Has an identical twin with depression | Has a non-identical twin with depression | Total |
| --- | --- | --- | --- |
| Shows symptoms of depression | 16 | 6 | 22 |
| Does not show symptoms of depression | 15 | 25 | 40 |
| Total | 31 | 31 | 62 |

    a)  How many degrees of freedom are there in this study?

    b)  The chi-squared value for this data is 7.05 (2 d.p.).  Using the table on page 62, is this data significantly different from chance at the 1% level?

    c)  What can you conclude from these results?

## My expected interest in this test is significantly less than my observed...

*The chi-squared test looks at the null hypothesis.  This means it assumes that there is no association between two variables — which is shown by the expected frequencies.  So if the observed frequencies are really different from the expected frequencies, your results are likely to be significant.  That's why you'll end up with a bigger chi-squared value.*

# Doing the Right Test

*You've seen some statistical tests, but that's only half the battle.*
*The tricky part is often deciding which one to use...*

## Different Tests Work for Different Kinds of Data

There are a few **kinds of data** you might come across. These are...

**Nominal data —**
Data that comes from recording the **number** of scores which fall into different categories.

Whether or not a person gambles is an example of nominal data, as is the toy a child picks in a preference test. You can analyse nominal data by recording its frequency.

**Ordinal data —**
Data that is a **number**, but that only tells you about an **order**, **without having a fixed scale.**

Imagine a group of people ranked in order of sociability. You know that the person ranked 1 is more sociable than the person ranked 7, but you don't know how much more sociable they are. This is ordinal data.

**Interval data —**
Data that is a **number**, with a **scale**, where **each unit** on the scale is the **same size.**

Weight is a kind of interval data — the difference between 64 kg and 65 kg is the same as the difference between 2 kg and 3 kg. You can use interval data in any of the tests for ordinal data in this book, as you can rank it in order.

*Interval data falls on a scientific scale, e.g. cm, seconds, ml, etc.*

So far in this section, you've seen how to analyse...

...data on **frequencies** for different groups...

| Gender | Preferred Toy | | Total |
|--------|-----|----------|-------|
| | Car | Soft toy | |
| Male | 18 | 12 | 30 |
| Female | 10 | 20 | 30 |
| Total | 28 | 32 | |

...data on how two **variables change together**...

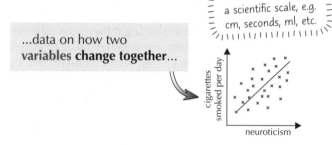

...data on differences **between groups** made up of **different individuals**...

...and data on differences **between groups** made up of the **same individuals** or **matched pairs** of individuals.

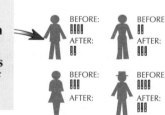

For different psychological studies, different tests will be appropriate, depending on **how the study has been designed**, and what **sort of data** has been collected. Luckily, there are some helpful rules for working out which test you should use...

## Think Carefully About Which Test to Use

Whenever you have some data to analyse, make sure you know the answers to these questions before you start:

1) Are you trying to find out if **two ordinal** (or interval) variables **change together**?
2) Are you trying to find out if one variable is **different between different conditions or groups**? If so...

- Is the variable something that's **ordinal** or **interval** (like test score), or do you have frequencies of something that's **nominal** (like preferred toy)?
- If the variable is **ordinal** (or interval), does the information in the two conditions pair up in some way (does the experiment have a repeated measures or matched pairs design)?

# Doing the Right Test

You can use this **handy table** to pick which test is right for your data...

These are **tests of difference** — they look to see if there is a significant difference in a variable between two or more conditions.

These are **tests of association** — they look to see if there is a significant relationship between two variables.

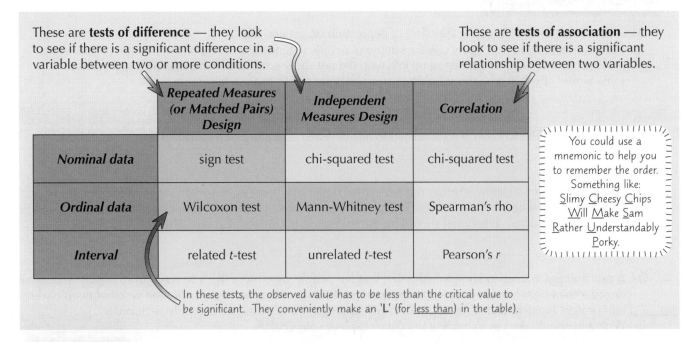

|  | Repeated Measures (or Matched Pairs) Design | Independent Measures Design | Correlation |
|---|---|---|---|
| **Nominal data** | sign test | chi-squared test | chi-squared test |
| **Ordinal data** | Wilcoxon test | Mann-Whitney test | Spearman's rho |
| **Interval** | related *t*-test | unrelated *t*-test | Pearson's *r* |

You could use a mnemonic to help you to remember the order. Something like:
Slimy Cheesy Chips Will Make Sam Rather Understandably Porky.

In these tests, the observed value has to be less than the critical value to be significant. They conveniently make an '**L**' (for <u>less than</u>) in the table).

## Worked Example

Two students studied how the number of words participants could recall from a list changed over time. They read a list of words to 7 participants and then measured how many they could recall after half an hour, and how many they recalled the next day. Their results are shown in the table on the right. One of the students analysed the results using a Mann-Whitney test. The other used a sign test. Both performed two-tailed tests and used a significance level of 0.05.

**Which analysis was the correct one to use for this study?**

| Number of words recalled | Participant | | | | | | |
|---|---|---|---|---|---|---|---|
| | 1 | 2 | 3 | 4 | 5 | 6 | 7 |
| After 30 mins | 15 | 8 | 13 | 11 | 17 | 18 | 7 |
| After 1 day | 11 | 2 | 12 | 10 | 16 | 9 | 6 |

**1** *Decide what the students are trying to do.*

They are trying to see if there is a significant difference in the number of words recalled at two different times.

So they'll want to use a **test of difference**.

**2** *Work out which experimental design is used.*

The same participants are in both groups.

It's a **repeated measures** design.

**3** *Now look at what type of data the students are collecting.*

The data collected is the number of words recalled.

It is **ordinal** data.

**4** *Use the table to see which test is right.*

The table shows that the Wilcoxon test was the right test to use.

|  | Repeated Measures (or Matched Pairs) Design | Independent Measures Design | Correlation |
|---|---|---|---|
| Nominal data | sign test | Chi-Squared test | Chi-Squared test |
| Ordinal data | Wilcoxon test | Mann-Whitney test | Spearman's rho |
| Interval | related *t*-test | unrelated *t*-test | Pearson's *r* |

# Doing the Right Test

## Practice Questions

Q1 A psychologist is investigating the effect of depression on general health.
She collects data on how many colds a sample of people diagnosed with depression caught in one winter, and the number of colds a group of people who did not show symptoms of depression caught in the same winter. Explain why she should use an unrelated *t*-test to analyse her results.

Q2 A researcher wants to know if IQ is related to age in years. Explain which statistical test he should use.

Q3 A scientist wanted to know whether rats performed better in a memory test when they were tested in low light conditions than when they were tested in high light conditions. He tested 8 rats, each under both low and high light conditions. Which test should he use to analyse his results? Explain why.

Q4 A psychologist wanted to know whether left-handed people were more likely to suffer from obsessive compulsive disorder than right-handed people. She used a questionnaire to collect information on whether people were left- or right-handed, and whether or not they had symptoms of obsessive compulsive disorder. What test should she use to analyse her data? Explain your choice.

Q5 A researcher wants to know whether anxiety levels are affected by caffeine. She collects data on anxiety levels in people with and without caffeine in their bloodstream, and compares the two groups using a Wilcoxon test. Assuming she used the correct statistical test, what can you say about the participants who took part in the two conditions?

Q6 In which statistical tests should the observed values be greater than or equal to the critical value, in order to show significance?

Q7 A psychologist was investigating how the temperature of a room influences people's reaction times. She collected the data shown in the table on the right. Based on this table, what test should she use to analyse her data? Explain your choice.

| Participant | Temperature in room (°C) | Reaction time (seconds) |
|---|---|---|
| 1 | 32 | 5.26 |
| 2 | 38 | 3.47 |
| 3 | 20 | 8.53 |
| 4 | 18 | 9.45 |
| 5 | 25 | 6.12 |

Q8 A researcher wanted to know whether attending a football match increases people's aggression levels.
Each participant in the study completed an aggression questionnaire before and after attending a football match where the team they support lost the game. The results are shown in the table below.
Aggression was measured on a scale of 1 to 100. (1 = least aggressive, 100 = most aggressive.)

| | Aggression level (1 – 100) | | | | | | | | |
|---|---|---|---|---|---|---|---|---|---|
| Before football match | 65 | 23 | 54 | 67 | 95 | 10 | 26 | 23 | 54 |
| After football match | 89 | 90 | 95 | 15 | 12 | 65 | 35 | 45 | 62 |

Which test should he use to analyse his data? Explain why.

## Do you choose the test, or does the test choose you...?

*It's one thing doing statistics when you've been told what to do, but picking a test for yourself is another matter. Learn the table on page 65, and make sure that whenever you decide on a test you can explain why it's the right one to use.*

# Answers

## Section One — Calculations

### Page 5 — Rounding

1 a) 0.04 g/cm³ (2 d.p.)
  b) 5.11 cm (3 s.f.)
2  $1.80^2 = 3.24$
  $95.03 \div 3.24 = 29.33024... = \textbf{29.3 (3 s.f.)}$
  *You have to round to 3 significant figures because that's the lowest number of significant figures in the question.*

### Page 7 — Standard Form

1

| 6120 | **0.00357** | **4 782 000** | 0.00000461 |
|---|---|---|---|
| **$6.12 \times 10^3$** | $3.57 \times 10^{-3}$ | $4.782 \times 10^6$ | **$4.61 \times 10^{-6}$** |

2 a) 0.00000183 g/ml
  b) $6.5 \times 10^{-7} = 0.00000065$
  $0.00000183 - 0.00000065 = 0.00000118 = \textbf{1.18} \times \textbf{10}^{-6}$ **g/ml**
  *Don't forget to convert your answer back to standard form.*

### Page 9 — Using Equations

1  $P = 3 \times 2 \times (8 - 3) = \textbf{30}$
2  $I = 6 \times (98 + 89 + 92) \div 18 = 1674 \div 18 = \textbf{93}$

### Page 11 — Tables of Data

1 a) 12 participants never played video games. 8 reported having 1-3 nights of disturbed sleep in the last month, and 2 reported more than 3 nights of disturbed sleep.
  so 12 – 2 – 8 = 2 had no nights of disturbed sleep.

| Frequency of playing video games | Number of nights of disturbed sleep in the last month | | |
|---|---|---|---|
| | None | 1-3 | More than 3 |
| Once a week or more | 3 | 7 | 2 |
| Less than once a week | 1 | 6 | 1 |
| Never | **2** | **8** | **2** |

  b) 6 + 1 = **7**
  c) 3 + 7 + 2 + 1 + 6 + 1 + 2 + 8 + 2 = **32**
  d) No. The number of nights of disturbed sleep in a month is about the same regardless of how often the participants played video games.

### Page 13 — Averages and Range

1 a) 15 – 2 = **13**
  b) 5
  c) In order, the scores are:
  2, 2, 3, 3, 4, 5, 5, 5, 6, 6, 7, 8, 8, 9, 12 ,15.
  The median score is halfway between the 8th and 9th scores.
  The 8th score is 5, the 9th score is 6.
  (6 + 5) ÷ 2 = 5.5. **The median score is 5.5**.
2 a) 20 – 8 = **12**
  b) (20 + 16 + 8 + 14 + 17 + 12 + 9) ÷ 7 = 13.7142857...
  = **13.7 to 1 d.p.**

3 a) 14
  b) In order, the scores are:
  10, 12, 13, 13, 14, 14, 14, 14, 15, 16, 16, 16, 18
  The middle value is 14, so **the median score is 14**.
  c) ((4 × 14) + (3 × 16) + (2 × 13) + 12 + 10 + 18 + 15)
  ÷ 13 = 185 ÷ 13 = 14.230769...
  = **14.23 to 2 d.p.**

### Page 15 — Ratios

1 a) 6 : 294. 6 ÷ 6 = 1, 294 ÷ 6 = 49.
  So in its simplest form, the ratio is **1 : 49**.
  *Make sure you give the ratio the right way round. 1:49 isn't the same as 49:1. The question asks for the ratio of people showing symptoms to those not showing symptoms, so the number with symptoms is first.*
  b) 3 : 3. In its simplest form, this is **1 : 1**.
2  40 : 47. 40 ÷ 40 = 1, 47 ÷ 40 = 1.175.
  In its simplest form, the ratio is **1 : 1.175**.
3 a) 1 : 1.5
  b) 30 × 1.5 = **45 females**.

### Page 18 — Fractions and Percentages

1 a) (35 ÷ 125) × 100 = **28%**
  b) $\dfrac{16 + 15}{62} = \dfrac{31}{62} = \dfrac{1}{2}$
  *You want the fraction of <u>women</u> in the survey who were aged between 26 and 35, so the bottom number is the total number of <u>women</u> who responded, not the overall total.*
2 a) $\dfrac{1}{250} \times 1000 = 1000 \div 250 = \textbf{4}$
  b) (0.05 ÷ 100) × 2000 = **1**
3  ((8.1 – 6.2) ÷ 8.1) × 100 = 23.4567... = **23.5% to 3 s.f.**

### Page 19 – Estimating

1  E.g. The difference in the mean score in Group 1 before and after the video was approximately 46 – 45 = 1.
  The difference in the mean score in Group 2 before and after the video was approximately 52 – 39 = 13.
  This suggests that there wasn't much difference between the aggression scores before and after the video in Group 1, whereas in Group 2 on average there was an increase in the aggression scores after compared to before the video.
  *You can't say 'watching boxing matches increases aggression'. You're just being asked to comment on the results of the study, not make a conclusion — you'd need more information to do that.*

## Section Two — Graph Skills

### Pages 22-23 — Bar Charts

1 a)

Obedience shown by participants.

  b) E.g. the data is in categories. / The data is not continuous.

# Answers

2 a) 36 s
b) 36 − 26 = **10 s**
c) E.g. on average, left-handed participants took less time to solve the puzzle than right-handed participants — their mean time taken is 10 seconds lower.
3 a) Therapy C
b) 6 − 2 = **4**
4 a) 19%
Be careful — squares on a bar chart don't always represent one unit.
b) i)  12% + 9% = **21%**
ii)  22% − 11% = **11%**
c) 100% − 35% = **65%**
5

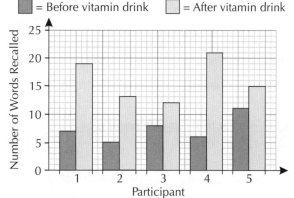

The effect of vitamin drinks on memory
■ = Before vitamin drink   □ = After vitamin drink

## Page 27 — Histograms

1 a) 3 − 2 = **1**
b) 2 + 5 + 1 + 4 + 3 = 15
(5 ÷ 15) × 100 = 33.33333... = **33%**
Have a look at page 16 if you need a reminder on calculating percentages.

2 a)

| Time Taken (minutes) | Freq. | Class Width | Frequency Density |
|---|---|---|---|
| $0 \le x < 2$ | 2 | 2 − 0 = **2** | 2 ÷ 2 = **1** |
| $2 \le x < 5$ | 6 | 5 − 2 = **3** | 6 ÷ 3 = **2** |
| $5 \le x < 10$ | 4 | 10 − 5 = **5** | 4 ÷ 5 = **0.8** |
| $10 \le x < 15$ | 3 | 15 − 10 = **5** | 3 ÷ 5 = **0.6** |
| $15 \le x < 25$ | 1 | 25 − 15 = **10** | 1 ÷ 10 = **0.1** |

b)
Frequencies of times taken to solve a test

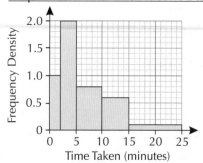

3 a) 0.1 − 0 = 0.1, 10 × 0.1 = 1
0.3 − 0.1 = 0.2, 30 × 0.2 = 6
0.4 − 0.3 = 0.1, 20 × 0.1 = 2
1 + 6 + 2 = **9**
b) 0.1 − 0 = 0.1, 10 × 0.1 = 1
0.3 − 0.1 = 0.2, 15 × 0.2 = 3
0.4 − 0.3 = 0.1, 30 × 0.1 = 3
0.5 − 0.4 = 0.1, 20 × 0.1 = 2
0.7 − 0.5 = 0.2, 5 × 0.2 = 1
1 + 3 + 3 + 2 + 1 = **10**

c) E.g. the reaction times for men were generally lower than the reaction times for women. / More males had a low reaction time than females.

## Page 31 — Scattergrams and Correlation

1 a) 9
b) E.g. there is no correlation in the data, so there is no relationship between aggression in children and the number of hours spent in day care.
2 a) positive correlation
b) 1.2 seconds
3 a)

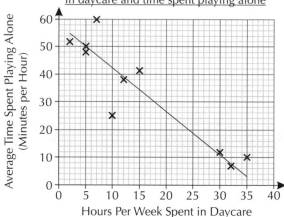

The relationship between time children spend in daycare and time spent playing alone

Remember, some of the results might be anomalous.
Just ignore these ones when you're drawing a line of best fit.
b) Your answer should be between 24 and 28 minutes per hour.
c) −0.855 is close to −1, so there is a strong negative relationship between time spent in day care and time spent playing alone. The negative correlation means that as the hours per week children spend in day care increases, the average time the children spend playing alone decreases.

## Page 33 — Distributions

1 a)

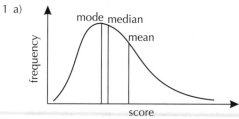

Remember — when mode < median < mean it's a positive skew.
b) A positively skewed distribution.
2  A negatively skewed distribution.
3

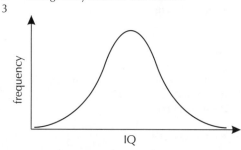

A normal distribution is symmetrical — it has mean = median = mode.

# Answers

## Section Three — Statistics
### Page 35 — Standard Deviation

1   $(5 - 10)^2 = 25$, $(15 - 10)^2 = 25$, $(10 - 10)^2 = 0$,
    $(11 - 10)^2 = 1$, $(9 - 10)^2 = 1$
    $25 + 25 + 0 + 1 + 1 = 52$
    $52 \div (5 - 1) = 13$
    $s = \sqrt{13} = 3.6055.... = $ **3.61 to 3 s.f.**

2   mean time $= (12 + 33 + 18 + 27 + 14 + 16) \div 6 = 20$
    $(12 - 20)^2 = 64$, $(33 - 20)^2 = 169$, $(18 - 20)^2 = 4$,
    $(27 - 20)^2 = 49$, $(14 - 20)^2 = 36$, $(16 - 20)^2 = 16$
    $64 + 169 + 4 + 49 + 36 + 16 = 338$
    $338 \div (6 - 1) = 67.6$
    $s = \sqrt{67.6} = 8.2219... = $ **8.2 to 2 s.f.**

3   E.g. on average, people aged 16-20 watched more television than people aged 21 to 25 and those aged 26 to 30. People aged 21-25 and 26-30 watched the same amount of television on average, but the amount of television watched per week varied more in the 21-25 age group.

### Page 37 — Writing Hypotheses

1 a) directional
  b) There will be no significant relationship between rates of depression and day length.
2 a) E.g. Alternative hypothesis: playing violent computer games increases the frequency of violent behaviour.
     Null hypothesis: playing violent computer games does not increase the frequency of violent behaviour.
  b) E.g. Alternative hypothesis: playing violent computer games changes the frequency of violent behaviour.
     Null hypothesis: playing violent computer games does not change the frequency of violent behaviour.

### Page 39 — Levels of Significance

1 a) No. ($p > 0.05$)
  b) There is no evidence that the psychic is better than chance at guessing the letter written on a piece of paper.

### Page 42 — The Sign Test

1 a) nominal
  b) 8
2 a) 0
  b) 2
3 a) The participants have been matched by gender and GCSE results, so it is a matched pairs design. The differences between the values in Year 12 and Year 13 can be converted into positive or negative signs, making them category/nominal data.
  b) E.g. year 12 students will not read significantly more books over one year than students in Year 13.
4 a) non-directional
  b) 9
     Participants 2, 6 and 7 all have a difference of zero, so their results aren't included.
  c) 1
  d)

| | Participant | 1 | 2 | 3 | 4 | 5 | 6 | 7 | 8 | 9 | 10 | 11 | 12 |
|---|---|---|---|---|---|---|---|---|---|---|---|---|---|
| Number of words recalled | Morning | 2 | 3 | 8 | 6 | 7 | 9 | 10 | 3 | 9 | 8 | 9 | 10 |
| | Evening | 6 | 3 | 5 | 4 | 6 | 9 | 10 | 2 | 7 | 10 | 10 | 6 |
| | Difference | 4 | 0 | 3 | 2 | 1 | 0 | 0 | 1 | 2 | 2 | 1 | 4 |
| | Sign | + | | − | − | − | | | − | − | + | + | − |

Total number of positive signs: 3
Total number of negative signs: 6
3 is smaller than 6, so the observed value is 3.
Since 3 is greater than 1, the results are **not significant** at $p \leq 0.05$.

### Pages 44-45 — Wilcoxon Test

1 a) 10
  b) 7
  c) 1
  d) 5
2   To use a Wilcoxon test, the same people need to have taken part in both conditions of a study.
3   One-tailed. She wants to know if the treatment is effective, which means her alternative hypothesis would be that CBT will reduce the symptoms of depression. This is a directional hypothesis.
4 a) directional
  b) E.g. there will be no significant difference in anxiety levels before and after an exercise programme.
  c) The critical value of $T$ is 2. 4 is greater than 2 so the result is not significant.
  d) E.g. regular exercise does not decrease anxiety levels, so the null hypothesis cannot be rejected.
5 a) The critical value of $T$ for this test is 2 (the hypothesis is non-directional so the two-tailed critical value is used).
     11 is greater than 2 so the results are not significant.
  b) E.g. the amount people eat is not affected by how much sleep they had the night before, therefore the null hypothesis cannot be rejected.

### Page 48 — Spearman's Rho

1 a) Very strong positive correlation.
  b) Very strong negative correlation.
  c) Moderate negative correlation.
  d) Weak positive correlation.
  e) No correlation.
2 a) 0.643
  b) 0.738
3 a) The critical value is 0.380. 0.278 is less than 0.380 so his results are **not significant**.
  b) E.g. he should conclude that there is no evidence to suggest that people who are more superstitious have higher anxiety levels. This means the null hypothesis cannot be rejected.

### Pages 50-51 — Pearson's r

1 a) Very strong negative correlation.
  b) Very weak positive correlation.
  c) Moderate positive correlation.
  d) Weak negative correlation.
  e) No correlation.
  f) Strong positive correlation.
2   There is a very weak positive correlation between people's heights and stress levels.
3 a) non-directional
  b) E.g. there is no relationship between the time taken to complete a puzzle task and IQ.
  c) $df = N - 2 = 12 - 2 = $ **10**
4 a) There is a strong positive correlation between Maths test scores and Science test scores.
  b) directional
  c) $df = N - 2 = 7 - 2 = $ **5**
  d) The critical value is 0.833. Since 0.759 is less than 0.833, the results are **not significant** at the 0.01 level.

# Answers

5 a) non-directional
   b) E.g. there is no relationship between intelligence and number of criminal offences among criminals.
   c) $df = N - 2 = 9 - 2 = 7$
   d) The critical value is 0.666. 0.910 is greater than 0.666, so the results are **significant** at the 0.05 level.

## *Page 54 — Related t-Test*

1 interval data
2 a) E.g. exercise has a significant effect on scores in a spelling test.
   This is a non-directional hypothesis, but you could also write a directional hypothesis. This would look something like — e.g. spelling ability will increase after the exercise drill.
   b) E.g. there is no significant difference in spelling ability before and after exercise.
   c) $df = N - 1 = 50 - 1 = 49$
3 a) non-directional
   b) E.g. there is no relationship between sleep deprivation and calorie consumption.
   c) $df = N - 1 = 22 - 1 = 21$
   d) 2.831
4 a) $df = N - 1 = 20 - 1 = 19$
   The hypothesis is directional, so a one-tailed test will be used. The critical value is 1.729.
   3.851 is greater than 1.729 so the results **are significant** at the 5% level.
   b) E.g. people who have just read a sad story in a newspaper are likely to give significantly more money to charity than people who have just read a happy story, so the null hypothesis can be rejected.
5 $df = N - 1 = 6 - 1 = 5$
   The hypothesis is directional, so a one-tailed test will be used. So, the critical value is 3.365.
   3.468 is more than 3.365 so the results are **significant** when $p \leq 0.01$.

## **Pages 56-57 — Unrelated t-Test**

1 a) The critical value is 3.707. 3.645 is less than 3.707, so the observed value is **not significant**.
   b) The critical value is 1.812. 1.965 is greater than 1.812, so the observed value is **significant**.
   c) The critical value is 3.499. 2.851 is less than 3.499, so the observed value is **not significant**.
   d) The critical value is 1.782. 1.782 is equal to 1.782, so the observed value is **significant**.
2 The same participants take part in both conditions, whereas an unrelated *t*-test should be used for different groups of participants.
3 a) E.g. students in Year 13 will perform significantly better on a memory test than students in Year 12.
   This is a directional hypothesis, but you could also write a non-directional hypothesis. This would look something like — e.g. there will be a significant difference between the memory performance of students in Year 12 and Year 13.
   b) E.g. students in Year 13 will not perform significantly differently on a memory test to students in Year 12.
4 a) non-directional
   b) E.g. there is no significant difference in average resting heart rate depending on whether someone lives in a village or a city.
   c) $df = N_X + N_Y - 2 = 7 + 9 - 2 = 14$

5 a) directional
   The psychologist wants to know if the computer programme is effective, which means that her alternative hypothesis would be that the programme will improve spelling.
   b) $df = N_X + N_Y - 2 = 7 + 7 - 2 = 12$
   c) 2.681
   d) E.g. using a computer programme for spelling has no effect on spelling ability.
   4.052 is more than 2.681, so the results are significant.
6 a) E.g. people who have used the new drug treatment will have a significantly lower blood pressure than people who haven't used the new drug treatment.
   b) E.g. the psychologist would need to use an independent measures design — so there will be two different groups of participants. The first group will use the new drug treatment, the second group will have no new treatment. The data gathered needs to be interval, so the psychologist should record participants' blood pressure following the treatment (or no treatment) over the course of one week.

## *Page 60 — Mann-Whitney Test*

1 a) 7
   b) 13
   c) 18
   d) 18
2 a) His results are significant. His value of $U$ is 4, which is less than the critical value of $U$ for a one-tailed test at the 0.05 significance level for two groups of 6 (which is 7).
   b) He should conclude that the new drug reduces the symptoms of anxiety and so the null hypothesis can be rejected.
3 a) directional
   b) E.g. children won't play with a toy for longer if they have seen a child of the same gender playing with the toy previously, compared to a child of the other gender.
   c) 5 is smaller than 31, so $U = $ **5**.
   d) Yes (the critical value of $U$ is 7).
   e) E.g. children will play with a toy for longer if they have seen a child of the same gender playing with the toy previously compared to a child of the opposite gender. This means the null hypothesis can be rejected.
4 10 is smaller than 71, so $U = $ **10**.
   The critical value of $U$ at the 0.05 level for these results is 21. 10 is less than 21, therefore these results do show that people who suffer from anorexia nervosa have significantly higher levels of anxiety than people who do not suffer from anorexia nervosa at the 5% level. Therefore, the null hypothesis can be rejected.

## *Page 63 — Chi-Squared Test*

1 a) The actual number of people in a given category.
   b) The number of people you'd expect to get in a given category if there was no relationship between the variables.
   c) Greater than or equal to.
2 a) 5.99
   b) 11.34
   c) 12.59
   d) 2.71
3 Her results are significant at the 0.05 level (the critical value of chi-squared is 3.84). She can conclude that there is a significant relationship between whether or not a parent is overweight and whether or not their children are. As such, she can then reject the null hypothesis.

4    No.  His research has a repeated measures design, as he collected data repeatedly from the same participants, so his results are not independent.

5  a)  $df = (2 - 1) \times (2 - 1) = \mathbf{1}$
   b)  Yes (the critical value for chi-squared is 6.64).
   c)  E.g. there is a significant relationship between someone showing symptoms of depression and whether their twin with depression is identical or non-identical.  This means the null hypothesis can be rejected.

## Page 66 — Doing the Right Test

1    She should use an unrelated $t$-test because she wants to know if a variable that has size / a variable with interval data (number of colds caught in a winter) is different between two groups made up of different participants (an independent measures design).

2    Spearman's rho.  He wants to know if there is a relationship between two variables that both have size / are both at least ordinal.

3    The Wilcoxon test.  He wants to know if there is a difference in a variable that has size / is at least ordinal (performance in a memory test) between two conditions (low and high light levels) where the same rats are used in each condition (a repeated measures design).

4    The chi-squared test.  She wants to know whether there is a difference in the number of right-handed people with symptoms of OCD and the number of left-handed people with symptoms of OCD, so she wants to find if there are differences in the frequency of a nominal condition (having or not having symptoms of OCD) between different groups.

5    The same people must have been used in the caffeine and no caffeine conditions.

6    The chi-squared test, Spearman's rho, related $t$-test, unrelated $t$-test and Pearson's $r$.

7    Pearson's $r$.  She wants to know if there is a relationship between two variables (temperature and reaction time) that are both interval (or ratio) data.

8    Wilcoxon test.  He wants to know if there is a difference in a variable with ordinal data (aggression level) between two conditions (before and after attending a football match) where the same participants are used in each condition (a repeated measures design).

# Glossary

## Alternative hypothesis

A prediction that there will be a significant relationship between two variables in a correlation, or that the independent variable will affect the dependent variable in an experiment.

## Anomalous result

A result that doesn't fit in with the rest of the results.

## Bar chart

A way of presenting data that falls into categories.

## BODMAS

The correct order to complete a calculation. It stands for Brackets, Order, Division and Multiplication, Addition and Subtraction.

## Chi-Squared test

A statistical test used with nominal data and independent samples to see if there is a significant difference between two or more frequencies.

## Correlation

The extent to which two variables rise and fall together, or that one rises as the other falls.

## Correlation coefficient

A numerical value worked out from a statistical test that shows how closely two variables are linked and the type of correlation they have.

## Critical value

A value which you compare the observed value from a statistical test against. This tells you whether or not the result is significant. Critical values are found in critical value tables.

## Dependent variable

The variable that you think is affected by changes in the independent variable, recorded in an experiment.

## Directional hypothesis

A hypothesis that expects a difference or correlation between two groups or conditions in scores of the dependent variable, stating the direction you expect the results to go.

## Distribution Curve

A graph showing the spread and position of averages of a set of data.

## Equation

A general rule showing how different quantities are related. Each quantity is shown by a different letter.

## Experimental hypothesis

A type of alternative hypothesis used in an experiment.

## Estimate

A rough or approximate answer to a calculation, made by rounding the numbers to get a simpler calculation.

## Frequency

The number of times something occurs, e.g. a participant answering 'yes' to a survey question.

## Frequency density

Plotted on a histogram. It is the frequency of a class divided by its class width.

## Fraction

A proportion which is written as one number over another. E.g. 1 out of 2 written as a fraction is $\frac{1}{2}$.

## Histogram

A way of presenting continuous data, where the area of the bars is proportional to their frequency.

## Independent variable

A variable manipulated by the researcher.

## Interval data

Numerical data with a scale where each unit is the same size.

## Line of best fit

A line drawn on a scattergram to fit the general pattern of the data which passes as close to as many points as possible. It helps the reader visualise the correlation between two variables.

## Mann-Whitney test

A statistical test used to see if there is a significant difference between two or more groups of values, where different participants have taken part in different conditions. It can be used for ordinal and interval data.

## Mean

What is normally meant by the average value in a data set. It's calculated by adding up all of the data values and then dividing the total by the number of values.

## Median

The middle value in a data set when they are arranged in size order.

## Mode

The most common value in a data set.

## Negative correlation

A type of correlation in which as one variable rises, the other falls.

## Negatively skewed distribution

Data has a negatively skewed distribution when the distribution curve has a long tail to the left. Then mean < median < mode.

## Nominal data

Data that can be split into categories.

## Non-directional hypothesis

A hypothesis that expects a correlation or difference between two groups or conditions in scores of the dependent variable, but it doesn't state the direction you expect the results to go.

## Normal distribution

Data is normally distributed when it's spread symmetrically either side of the mean. Then mean = median = mode.

# Glossary

**Null hypothesis**
What you assume to be true in an experiment. It claims there will be no relationship or difference between the groups or conditions in scores of the dependent variable.

**Observed value**
The value, or test statistic, calculated by carrying out a statistical test.

**Ordinal data**
Numerical data which can be ranked in order.

**Pearson's *r* test**
A statistical test used to find the strength and direction of a correlation between two variables, and whether the correlation is significant. Data must be interval.

**Percentage**
A number written as an amount out of 100.

**Positive correlation**
A type of correlation in which the variables rise and fall together.

**Positively skewed distribution**
Data has a positively skewed distribution when the distribution curve has a long tail to the right. Then mode < median < mean.

**Probability**
How likely something is to happen.

**Proportion**
A part of a whole. For example, a test score is the proportion of questions that were answered correctly (e.g. 18 out of 20).

**Range**
The difference between the smallest and the largest values in a data set.

**Ratio**
A way of comparing two quantities. Ratios are written in the form *a* : *b*. E.g. a ratio of males to females of 1 : 2 would mean there were 2 females for every 1 male.

**Related *t*-test**
A statistical test used to see if there's a significant difference between two conditions in a repeated measures or matched pairs design. Data must be interval.

**Rounding**
Writing a number with lots of digits as a number with fewer digits, to a certain number of decimal places or significant figures.

**Sample**
Participants from the population that should represent the target group.

**Scattergram**
A way of plotting points and visualising relationships between variables.

**Sigma**
A mathematical sign meaning 'sum of'. It looks like this: $\sum$.

**Sign test**
A statistical test used to see if there is a significant difference between two sets of scores. You must be able to compare the scores by splitting them into ones with a positive difference and ones with a negative difference. This is nominal data.

**Significance level**
The 'level of proof' that you're looking for before you accept that your results are likely to be down to chance.

**Significant result**
A result that's very unlikely to be due to chance. If a result is significant you can reject the null hypothesis.

**Simplest form**
A ratio or fraction written in its simplest form is one written using the smallest numbers possible.

**Spearman's rho**
A test statistic used to see the strength and direction of an relationship between two variables, and whether the relationship is significant. Both variables must have ordinal data.

**Standard deviation**
A measure of spread.

**Standard form**
A way of writing numbers using powers of 10 — it's a shorter way of writing very large or very small numbers that contain lots of zeros.

**Test statistic**
A number that you calculate during a statistical test, which you can use to judge whether your results are significant.

**Two-way table**
A table showing frequencies across two sets of categories (for example gender and test score).

**Unrelated *t*-test**
A statistical test used to see if there is a significant difference between two conditions in an independent measures design. Data must be interval.

**Variable**
A factor in an experiment that does not have a fixed value. It can be controlled, changed or measured.

**Wilcoxon test**
A statistical test used to see if there is a significant difference between two conditions in a repeated measures or matched pairs design. It can be used for ordinal and interval data.

***x*-axis**
The axis that runs along the bottom of a graph. It's where you'd normally put the independent variable.

***y*-axis**
The axis that runs up the side of a graph. It's where you'd normally put the dependent variable.

# Index

PYMR71